It's another Quality Book from CGP

This book is for anyone doing **Cambridge International Level 1/Level 2 Certificate in Mathematics** or the **Cambridge IGCSE® in Mathematics**.

It gives you all the important information as clearly and concisely as possible — along with some daft bits to try and make the whole experience at least vaguely entertaining for you.

Extended

This book is suitable for both Core and Extended Curriculum candidates. The material which is required only for the Extended Curriculum is clearly indicated in green boxes like this.

In addition, the Extended Curriculum questions in the book are printed in green.

Extended

What CGP is all about

Our sole aim here at CGP is to produce the highest quality books — carefully written, immaculately presented and dangerously close to being funny.

Then we work our socks off to get them out to you — at the cheapest possible prices.

Contents

Published by CGP

Written by Richard Parsons

Editors: Mary Falkner, Paul Jordin and Sharon Keeley-Holden

With thanks to Rosie Gillham, Jane Appleton and James Welham for the proofreading

IGCSE® is a registered trademark of Cambridge International Examinations.

This book is not endorsed by Cambridge International Examinations.

ISBN: 978 1 84762 557 1

www.cgpbooks.co.uk

Clipart from Corel®   Printed by Elanders Ltd, Newcastle upon Tyne.

Types of Number

A nice easy start to the book. I can't promise things won't get harder later on, so enjoy it while you can...

1) NATURAL NUMBERS

1) The natural numbers are the <u>whole numbers</u> that are <u>greater than zero</u>.
2) They're just the numbers that you normally use when you're counting things: <u>1</u>, <u>2</u>, <u>3</u>, <u>4</u>, <u>5</u>, etc.

2) INTEGERS

An <u>integer</u> is just any <u>whole number</u>. It doesn't matter if it's less than zero, greater than zero, or zero itself — if it's a whole number, then it's an integer.

$$...-4 \quad -3 \quad -2 \quad -1 \quad 0 \quad 1 \quad 2 \quad 3 \quad 4...$$

3) SQUARE NUMBERS

<u>Squaring</u> a number means '<u>multiplying it by itself</u>': $P \times P = P^2$
The square of any integer is called a '<u>square number</u>':

(1x1) (2x2) (3x3) (4x4) (5x5) (6x6) (7x7) (8x8) (9x9) (10x10) (11x11) (12x12) (13x13) (14x14) (15x15)

| 1 | 4 | 9 | 16 | 25 | 36 | 49 | 64 | 81 | 100 | 121 | 144 | 169 | 196 | 225... |

3 5 7 9 11 13 15 17 19 21 23 25 27 29

Note that the <u>DIFFERENCES</u> between the <u>square numbers</u> are all the ODD numbers.

4) CUBE NUMBERS

<u>Cubing</u> a number means '<u>multiplying it by itself 3 times</u>': $J \times J \times J = J^3$
The cube of any integer is called a '<u>cube number</u>':

Well, strictly there are only two × signs, but you know what I mean.

(1×1×1) (2×2×2) (3×3×3) (4×4×4) (5×5×5) (6×6×6) (7×7×7) (8×8×8) (9×9×9) (10×10×10)

| 1 | 8 | 27 | 64 | 125 | 216 | 343 | 512 | 729 | 1000... |

5) RATIONAL NUMBERS

Most numbers you deal with are rational. They can always be written as <u>fractions</u>. You'll come across them in 3 different forms:

1) <u>Whole numbers</u>, e.g. 4 ($=\frac{4}{1}$), −5 ($=\frac{-5}{1}$), −12 ($=\frac{-12}{1}$)
2) <u>Fractions</u> p/q, where p and q are integers (and q is not zero), e.g. $\frac{1}{4}$, $-\frac{1}{2}$, $\frac{3}{4}$
3) <u>Terminating or recurring decimals</u>, e.g. 0.125 ($=\frac{1}{8}$), 0.33333... ($=\frac{1}{3}$), −0.143143143... ($=\frac{-143}{999}$)

6) IRRATIONAL NUMBERS

1) Irrational numbers are messy. They're numbers that <u>can't</u> be written as fractions.
2) They are always <u>never-ending non-repeating decimals</u>. π is irrational.
3) Lots of <u>square roots</u> and <u>cube roots</u> are irrational numbers.
   For example: $\sqrt{2} = 1.414213562...$ and $\sqrt[3]{7} = 1.912931183...$

These decimal bits <u>never end</u> and don't contain any <u>repeating patterns</u> — so you can never write them out <u>exactly</u>.

7) REAL NUMBERS

1) <u>All rational numbers</u> and <u>all irrational numbers</u> are <u>real numbers</u>.
2) That means <u>all</u> the different types of numbers you'll come across in this course are <u>real numbers</u>. Natural numbers, integers, square numbers, square roots, fractions and decimals are all real numbers.

And there's me thinking numbers were a kind of squiggly shape...

There, that wasn't too bad, was it. Now you need to <u>learn the page</u>. When you've got it, try these questions...
1) Write down three natural numbers, three integers, three square numbers, and three real numbers.
2) Write down some examples of each of the three different forms of rational numbers.

Prime Numbers

"Hang on a minute," I hear you cry. "What about prime numbers — why haven't they come up yet?" Well you're in luck, my poor revising friend...

1) Basically, PRIME Numbers Don't Divide by anything

...and that's the easiest way to think of them. (Strictly speaking, they divide by themselves and 1).
So prime numbers are all the numbers that don't come up in times tables:

2 3 5 7 11 13 17 19 23 29 31 37 ...

As you can see, they're an awkward-looking bunch (that's because they don't divide by anything!).

For example:

The only numbers that multiply to give 7 are 1×7
The only numbers that multiply to give 31 are 1×31

In fact the only way to get ANY PRIME NUMBER is $1 \times$ ITSELF

2) They End in 1, 3, 7 or 9

1) 1 is NOT a prime number.
2) The first four prime numbers are 2, 3, 5 and 7.
3) Prime numbers end in 1, 3, 7 or 9 (2 and 5 are the only exceptions to this rule).
4) But NOT ALL numbers ending in 1, 3, 7 or 9 are primes, as shown here:
(Only the circled ones are primes)

⑪	⑬	⑰	⑲
21	㉓	27	㉙
㉛	33	㊲	39
㊶	㊸	㊼	49
51	(53)	57	(59)
(61)	63	(67)	69

3) How to Find Prime Numbers — a very simple method

For a number to be prime:

1) It must end in 1, 3, 7, or 9.
2) It WON'T DIVIDE by any of the primes below the value of its own square root.

If something like this comes up on a question where you're told not to use your calculator, you'll have to start by estimating the square root — see page 31.

EXAMPLE: "Decide whether or not 233 is a prime number."

1) Does it end in 1, 3, 7 or 9? Yes
2) Find its square root: $\sqrt{233} = 15.264$
3) List all primes which are less than this square root: 2, 3, 5, 7, 11 and 13
4) Divide all of these primes into the number under test:

$233 \div 3 = 77.6667$ $233 \div 7 = 33.2857$
$233 \div 11 = 21.181818$ $233 \div 13 = 17.923077$ (it obviously won't divide by 2 or 5.)

5) Since none of these divide cleanly into 233 then it is a prime number. Easy peasy.

Two's an odd prime — it's even, which makes it odd. Hmm...

OK, as before learn all the main points on the page, then cover it up and write it all down. Then try these...

1) Write down the first 15 prime numbers (without looking them up).
2) Find all the prime numbers between a) 100 and 110 b) 200 and 210 c) 500 and 510

Common Factors

I'm afraid it's time for some good ol' fashioned <u>maths terms</u>. It was bound to happen sooner or later...

Numbers divide Exactly by their Factors

For example, 44 ÷ 11 = 4, so 11 is <u>a factor of</u> 44.

The <u>FACTORS</u> of a number are all the numbers that <u>DIVIDE INTO IT</u>.

There's a special method you can use to find <u>ALL</u> the factors of a number...

EXAMPLE 1: "Find all the factors of 24."

1) Start off with 1 × the number itself, then try 2 ×, then 3 × and so on, listing the pairs in rows like this.
2) Try each one in turn, putting a dash if it doesn't divide exactly.
3) Eventually, when you get a number <u>REPEATED</u>, you <u>STOP</u>.
4) So the <u>FACTORS OF 24</u> are <u>1,2,3,4,6,8,12,24</u>

Increasing by 1 each time

```
1 × 24
2 × 12
3 × 8
4 × 6
5 × −
6 × 4
```

A Common Factor is a Shared Factor of Two Numbers

If two or more numbers share a <u>factor</u>, then it's known as a <u>COMMON FACTOR</u> of those numbers.
For example, 12 ÷ 4 = 3 and 20 ÷ 4 = 5, so 4 is a <u>common factor</u> of 12 and 20.

You can find the common factors of a group of numbers like <u>this</u>:

1) <u>LIST</u> all the <u>FACTORS</u> of <u>ALL</u> the numbers.
2) Circle any numbers that are in <u>ALL the lists</u>.

EXAMPLE: Find the common factors of 36, 54 and 72

Factors of 36 are: ①, ②, ③, 4, ⑥, ⑨, 12, ⑱, 36
Factors of 54 are: ①, ②, ③, ⑥, ⑨, ⑱, 27, 54
Factors of 72 are: ①, ②, ③, 4, ⑥, 8, ⑨, 12, ⑱, 24, 36, 72

So the common factors of 36, 54, and 72 are: 1, 2, 3, 6, 9 and 18.

The Biggest number on the list is the Highest Common Factor

You might come across the term '<u>Highest Common Factor</u>' too — all it means is <u>this</u>:

The <u>BIGGEST</u> number that will <u>DIVIDE INTO ALL</u> the numbers in question.

1) To find the <u>highest common factor</u>, use the same method as you did to find all the common factors — <u>list all the factors</u> of all the numbers, and circle any numbers that appear in <u>all the lists</u>.
2) The <u>biggest number</u> that you've circled is the highest common factor of the numbers.
So, in the example above, the highest common factor of 36, 54 and 72 is <u>18</u>.

I wanna live like common factors. I wanna do whatever common factors do...

I wanna sle... actually, best not go there. You need to learn what common factors are, and <u>how to find them</u>.
Turn over and write it all down. And after that, here are some lovely questions for you to do — bonus.

1) Find all the common factors of 36 and 84.
2) Find all the common factors of 56 and 104. What's their highest common factor?

Common Multiples

And now, for a thrilling sequel to common factors, it's... wait for it... common multiples.

A Multiple is the Product of Two Numbers

> The <u>MULTIPLES</u> of a number are simply its <u>TIMES TABLE</u>:

So the <u>multiples of 5</u> are... 5 10 15 20 25 30 35 40 ...
And the <u>multiples of 13</u> are... 13 26 39 52 65 78 91 104 ...

A Common Multiple is a Multiple of two Different Numbers

If the <u>same number</u> appears in the <u>times tables</u> of two or more different numbers,
then it's known as a <u>COMMON MULTIPLE</u> of those numbers.

For example, 6 × 4 = 24 and 8 × 3 = 24, so 24 is a <u>common multiple</u> of 6 and 8.

Here's how you can find some common multiples for a group of numbers:

> 1) <u>LIST MULTIPLES</u> of <u>ALL</u> the numbers.
> 2) Circle any numbers that are in <u>ALL the lists</u>.

Don't try to list <u>all</u> the common multiples — you'll be there for ever (literally). Stop when you've found as many as you need.

EXAMPLE: Find four common multiples of 6 and 9.

Multiples of 6 are: 6, 12, (18,) 24, 30, (36) 42, 48, (54) 60, 66, (72)...
Multiples of 9 are: 9, (18,) 27, (36) 45, (54) 63, (72) 81, 90 ...
So 18, 36, 54 and 72 are all <u>common multiples</u> of 6 and 9.

The Smallest number on the list is the Lowest Common Multiple

'<u>Lowest Common Multiple</u>' might sound a bit complicated but all it really means is this:

> The <u>SMALLEST</u> number that will <u>DIVIDE BY ALL</u> the numbers in question.

In other words, it's just the <u>smallest number</u> on your list of <u>common multiples</u>.
So to find the lowest common multiple, you just do this:

1) <u>List multiples</u> of both numbers, and circle any numbers that appear in <u>both lists</u>.
2) The <u>first number</u> that you've circled is the lowest common multiple of the numbers.

EXAMPLE: Find the lowest common multiple of 6 and 7
Multiples of 6 are: 6, 12, 18, 24, 30, 36, (42,) 48, 54, 60, 66, 72, 78, (84)..
Multiples of 7 are: 7, 14, 21, 28, 35, (42,) 49, 56, 63, 70, 77, (84,) 91...

> So the <u>lowest common multiple</u> of 6 and 7 is <u>42</u>.

Takes me back to my youth, scrumping multiples from the orchards...

...innocent times, they were. Right, learn how to find <u>common multiples</u> and then do these questions:
1) List the first 10 multiples of 7.
2) Find four common multiples of 4 and 12.
3) Find the lowest common multiple of 15 and 20.

Square Roots and Cube Roots

Take a deep breath, and get ready to tackle this page. Good luck with it, I'll be rootin' for ya...

Square Roots

Finding the <u>square root</u> is the <u>reverse of squaring</u>.

The best way to think of it is this:

> **'Square Root' means**
> **'What Number Times by Itself gives...'**

<u>Example</u>: 'Find the square root of 49' (i.e. 'Find $\sqrt{49}$')

To do this you should say "what number times by itself gives 49?"

And the answer, of course, is <u>7</u>.

Square Roots can be Positive or Negative

When you take the square root of a number, the answer can actually be <u>positive</u> or <u>negative</u>...
You always get a positive and negative version of the <u>same number</u>.

E.g. $x^2 = 4$ gives $x = \pm\sqrt{4} = +2$ or -2

To understand why, look at what happens when you work backwards
by squaring the answers: $2^2 = 2 \times 2 = 4$ but also $(-2)^2 = (-2) \times (-2) = 4$

> On your calculator, <u>it's easy to find the positive square root</u>
> using the <u>SQUARE ROOT BUTTON</u>:   Press $\sqrt{}$ 49 = <u>7</u>

Cube Roots

Finding the <u>cube root</u> is the <u>reverse of cubing</u>.

Think of this as:

> **'Cube Root' means 'What Number**
> **Times by Itself THREE TIMES gives...'**

That's only two × signs, remember:
number × number × number.

<u>Example</u>: "Find the cube root of 64" (i.e 'Find $\sqrt[3]{64}$')

You should say "What number times by itself three times gives 64?"
And after a few guesses, the answer is <u>4</u>.

Unlike square roots, there's
only <u>one answer</u>. A <u>positive
number cubed</u> is always
<u>positive</u>, and a <u>negative number
cubed</u> is always <u>negative</u>.

> <u>Or</u> on your calculator just use the <u>cube root button</u>:
> Press $\sqrt[3]{}$ 64 = <u>4</u>

"Cue brute", that's what I call Charley when I play him at snooker...

<u>LEARN</u> the <u>definitions in the blue boxes</u> and the <u>methods for finding roots</u>. Then turn the page and write it all down.

1) Use your calculator to find to 2 d.p. a) $\sqrt{200}$ b) $\sqrt[3]{8000}$
   For a) what is the other value that your calculator didn't give?
2) a) If $g^2 = 36$, find g.   b) If $b^3 = 64$, find b.   c) If $4 \times r^2 = 36$, find r.

Order of Operations

When you're faced with a <u>multi-step calculation</u>, you need to know what <u>order</u> to do the different parts in. That's where the <u>order of operations</u> comes in...

The Order of Operations

If you're doing a calculation that's got lots of <u>steps</u> in it, you have to do them in the <u>right order</u>. There's a <u>set of rules</u> that tells you what the right order is — it's called the <u>order of operations</u>.

The way to remember the order of operation is using BODMAS. This stands for:

<u>B</u>rackets, <u>O</u>ther, <u>D</u>ivision, <u>M</u>ultiplication, <u>A</u>ddition, <u>S</u>ubtraction

BODMAS tells you to: 1)   Sort out any bits in <u>Brackets</u> first.

2)   Then deal with <u>Other</u> things, like <u>powers</u> and <u>square roots</u>.

3)   Next do any <u>Division</u> or <u>Multiplication</u> steps (going from <u>left to right</u>).

4)   Finally do any <u>Additions</u> and <u>Subtractions</u> (going from <u>left to right</u>).

> <u>**EXAMPLE:**</u> $T = (P - 7)^2 + -2 \times 3$
> Find the value of T when P = 4.
>
> 1)   Put the value of P into the equation: $T = (4 - 7)^2 - 2 \times 3$
> 2)   Then work it out <u>in stages</u>: $= (-3)^2 - 2 \times 3$
> $= 9 - 6$
> $= \underline{3}$
>
> > <u>BODMAS in action</u>:
> > <u>Brackets</u> worked out...
> > ...then <u>squared</u>,...
> > ...the <u>multiplication</u> is done first...
> > ...then the <u>subtraction</u>.

Brackets are Really Important in BODMAS

Brackets have <u>top priority</u> in BODMAS — <u>anything</u> in brackets is worked out <u>before</u> anything else happens to it. By adding brackets, you can <u>change the order</u> that the steps are done in.

> Imagine that you want to ask somebody to <u>add 19 to 26</u>, and <u>divide the result by 3</u>.
>
> • You could write $19 + 26 \div 3$. But BODMAS says to do <u>division first</u>, and <u>then addition</u>. They'll look at the expression and say $19 + 26 \div 3 = 19 + 8.7 = 27.7$
>
> • If you want them to do the <u>addition first</u>, and <u>then the division</u>, you need to put <u>brackets</u> in, like this: $(19 + 26) \div 3$. BODMAS tells you to do the bits in <u>brackets first</u>. So that's $(19 + 26) \div 3 = 45 \div 3 = 15$.

This is <u>really important</u> to remember when you're using a <u>calculator</u>. They <u>always</u> follow the BODMAS rules — so you <u>must</u> use brackets to tell your calculator which bits of the calculation to do <u>first</u>.

<u>Remember — order the that you things do in really important is...</u>

Remember to <u>practise</u> everything you've just learnt on this page. Start with this question.

1)   Calculate the following to 2 d.p.   a) $4 + 3^2 \times (8 \div 4) - 10$ b) $\dfrac{74^2 - 10^3}{\sqrt{49} \times 2^4}$

Using Calculators

This page is full of lovely calculator tricks to save you a lot of button-bashing.

The Fraction Button: [a$\frac{b}{c}$]

Use this as much as possible in the exams — it'll really save you time.
It's very easy, so make sure you know how to use it properly — you'll lose a lot of marks if you don't:

1) To enter $\frac{1}{4}$ press [1] [a$\frac{b}{c}$] [4]

2) To enter $1\frac{3}{5}$ press [1] [a$\frac{b}{c}$] [3] [a$\frac{b}{c}$] [5]

3) To work out $\frac{1}{5} \times \frac{3}{4}$ press [1] [a$\frac{b}{c}$] [5] [×] [3] [a$\frac{b}{c}$] [4] [=]

4) To reduce a fraction to its lowest terms enter it and then press [=].
   E.g. $\frac{9}{12}$ — [9] [a$\frac{b}{c}$] [12] [=]   [3⌐4] = $\frac{3}{4}$

5) To convert between mixed and top-heavy fractions press [SHIFT] [a$\frac{b}{c}$].
   E.g. $2\frac{3}{8}$ — [2] [a$\frac{b}{c}$] [3] [a$\frac{b}{c}$] [8] [=] [SHIFT] [a$\frac{b}{c}$] which gives $\frac{19}{8}$

The MEMORY BUTTONS ([STO] Store, [RCL] Recall)

These are really useful for keeping a number you've just calculated,
so you can use it again shortly afterwards.

E.g. Find $\dfrac{840}{15 + 12\sin 40}$ — just work out the bottom line first and stick it in the memory.

So press [15] [+] [12] [SIN] [40] [=] and then [STO] [M] to keep the result of the bottom line in the memory.
Then you simply press [840] [÷] [RCL] [M] [=], and the answer is 36.98.

The memory buttons might work a bit differently on your calculator. Note, if your calculator
has an 'Ans' button, you can do the same thing as above using that instead
— the Ans button gives you the result you got when you last pressed the '=' button.

Check Your Answers using Estimation

When you use a calculator to find the answer to a question, you should check that answer using
estimation. This is to get an idea of whether your answer's roughly right — if the estimate's
miles different from your answer, you know something's gone wrong. This is all you need to do:

> 1) ROUND EVERYTHING OFF to nice easy CONVENIENT NUMBERS.
> 2) Then WORK OUT THE ANSWER using those nice easy numbers
>   — and see if it roughly matches your calculator answer.

Example: Find 3119 × 1.97   Calculator shows: [6144.43]
Do 3000 × 2 in your head as a check. 3000 × 2 = 6000.
That's pretty close — so you can be pretty sure that your answer's right.

Learn these two pages, store, then recall...

Learn your calculator buttons. Practise until you can answer all of these without having to refer back:
1) Convert these into top-heavy fractions: a) 2¾ b) 16½ c) 8¼
2) Explain what [STO] and [RCL] do and give an example of using them.

Standard Form

Standard form (or 'standard index form') is only really useful for writing <u>VERY BIG</u> or <u>VERY SMALL</u> numbers in a more convenient way, e.g.

$\qquad$ 56 000 000 000 would be 5.6×10^{10} in standard form.

$\qquad$ 0.000 000 003 45 would be 3.45×10^{-9} in standard form.

But <u>ANY NUMBER</u> can be written in standard form and you need to know how to do it:

What it Actually is:

The Three Rules
1. Wash behind your ears.
2. Don't feed a decimal point after midnight.
3. Never take maths advice from a duck.

A number written in standard form must <u>ALWAYS</u> be in <u>EXACTLY</u> this form:

$$A \times 10^{n}$$

This <u>number</u> must <u>always</u> be <u>BETWEEN 1 AND 10</u>.

(The fancy way of saying this is: $1 \leq A < 10$ — they sometimes write that in Exam questions — don't let it put you off, just remember what it means).

This number is just the <u>NUMBER OF PLACES</u> the <u>Decimal Point</u> moves.

Learn The Three Rules:

1) The <u>front number</u> must always be <u>BETWEEN 1 AND 10</u>.

2) The power of 10, n, is purely: <u>HOW FAR THE D.P. MOVES</u>.

3) n is <u>+ve</u> for <u>BIG</u> numbers, n is <u>−ve</u> for <u>SMALL</u> numbers.

(This is much better than rules based on which way the D.P. moves.)

Two Very Simple Examples:

1) "Express 35 600 in standard form."

<u>METHOD:</u>

1) Move the D.P. until 35 600 becomes 3.56 ($1 \leq A < 10$)
2) The D.P. has moved 4 places so n=4, giving: 10^4
3) 35 600 is a BIG number so n is +4, not −4

<u>ANSWER:</u>
3.5600
$= \underline{3.56 \times 10^4}$

2) "Express 0.0000623 in standard form."

<u>METHOD:</u>

1) The D.P. must move <u>5 places to give 6.23</u> ($1 \leq A < 10$),
2) So the power of 10 is 5
3) Since 0.0000623 is a <u>SMALL NUMBER</u> it must be 10^{-5} not 10^{+5}.

<u>ANSWER:</u>
0.0000623
$= \underline{6.23 \times 10^{-5}}$

Standard Form

Learn how Your Calculator Displays Standard Form

Different calculators will show answers in standard form in different ways. For example:

2.5×10^{15} might look like this: `2.5¹⁵`   Or this: `2.5E15`

You should ALWAYS write your answers in the form 2.5×10^{15} (2.5¹⁵ means something <u>completely different</u>).
So you need to <u>understand</u> what the display on <u>your own calculator</u> means.

Four More Very Important Examples

1) The Calculator's Scientific Mode

This mode <u>gives all numbers in standard form</u> to a specified number of sig fig.
To get into this mode, press `MODE` and select SCI from one of the menus you get.

It'll ask you for the number of sig figs to display, something like this: `SCI 0-9?`
So if you choose 4, all your answers will be displayed to 4 sig fig.

<u>EXAMPLE</u>: $565 \div 3$ would give `188.3333333` in normal mode,

...or `1.883⁰²` in 4 sig fig mode.

2) What is 146.3 million in standard form?

The two favourite wrong answers for this are:

1) 146.3×10^6 — which is kind of right but it's not in <u>STANDARD FORM</u>
   because 146.3 is not between 1 and 10 (i.e. $1 \leq A < 10$ has not been done)

2) 1.463×10^6 — this one <u>is</u> in standard form but it's not big enough.

This is a very typical Exam question, which <u>too many people get wrong</u>.

<u>Take your time</u> and <u>do it in two stages</u> like this: <u>ANSWER</u>: 146.3 million = 146 300 000 = $\underline{1.463 \times 10^8}$

3) Remember, 10⁵ means 1×10⁵

To enter 10^5 into the calculator you must remember it's actually 1×10^5 and press `1` `EXP` `5`

<u>EXAMPLE</u>: A nanometre is 10^{-9} m. How many nanometres are there in 0.35 m?
ANSWER: $0.35 \div (1 \times 10^{-9})$, so press `0.35` `÷` `1` `EXP` `(-)` `9` `=` = 3.5×10^8.

<u>EXP</u> stands for <u>exponential</u> — this key fills in the "...times ten to the power..." bit of the calculation.

4) The 'Googol' is 10¹⁰⁰ and is a pest

It's a pest because it goes off the scale of your calculator, so you have to do it 'by hand' — which means that it often turns up in Exam questions. Make sure you <u>learn</u> how to deal with example like this:

<u>EXAMPLE</u>: <u>Express 56 googols in standard form.</u>
ANS: 56 googols is $56 \times 10^{100} = 5.6 \times 10 \times 10^{100} = 5.6 \times 10^{101}$.

Split the 56 into 5.6 × 10 and then <u>combine the powers of 10</u>

How come I can get Google™ on my phone, but not on my calculator..?

Learn the <u>three rules</u> and the <u>four important examples</u>, then turn over and <u>write them down</u>. Then lookie here...

1) a) Express 0.854 million in standard index form.   b) Express 4.56×10^{-3} as an ordinary number.
2) a) Work out $(3.2 \times 10^7) \div (1.6 \times 10^{-4})$.   b) How many nanometres are there in 10^{-1} m?
3) Write down 650 googols in standard form.

Sets

If you like collections of things, you'll love <u>sets</u> — because... well... they're collections of things.

A Set is a Group of Objects

1) A <u>SET</u> is just a maths word for a <u>collection of objects</u>, or <u>numbers</u>. All of the things in a set have some kind of connection. These are all examples of sets:

| Prime numbers | Negative numbers | Odd numbers between 2 and 16 | Things that are red |

2) Each individual object in a set is called an <u>ELEMENT</u>. So 7 is <u>an element</u> of the set of prime numbers, and a strawberry is <u>an element</u> of the set of things that are red.

3) You can use a <u>capital letter</u> to stand for <u>a set</u>, e.g. A = the set of numbers that are multiples of four. This just makes it quicker and easier to write about the set later.

4) A <u>lower case letter</u> stands for <u>an element</u> in the set, e.g. "x is in set A, so x must be an even number".

You can Describe a set by Describing Its Elements

If you want to tell somebody what <u>elements</u> are in a <u>set</u>, then there are two ways to do it.

1) You can write out a <u>complete list</u> of all the elements, like this:
{1, 3, 5, 7, 9, 11, 13, 15, 17, 19, 21, 23, 25, 27, 29} The curly brackets are there to tell you that this is a set.

2) Or you can write out the <u>rule</u> that connects the elements: {odd numbers between 0 and 30}

You still need curly brackets here to show that this is a set too.

You can write Rules in Numbers and Symbols too

It's fine to write out the description of the elements of a set in <u>words</u>, like the example in point 2. But you'll often see <u>numbers and symbols</u> used to write the description too.

{x: x is a negative number} — This means that if x stands for any negative number, then the elements of the set are all the possible values of x.

{x: x < 0} — This is a different way of writing the same thing — saying that x < 0 means that x must be a negative number.

{(x,y): y = 2x + 2} — This one is a set of all the points that lie on the line $y = 2x + 2$. Each element is a pair of coordinates — that's what the (x, y) bit means.

Learn how to write about sets using Set Notation

Here are four handy little bits of <u>set notation</u> — learn what these symbols mean, and how to use them.

$\in$ **...IS AN ELEMENT OF...** Rather than writing "5 is an element of Set A", you can just write "5 $\in$ A"

$\notin$ **...IS NOT AN ELEMENT OF...** This is the opposite — so "2 $\notin$ A" means "2 is not an element of Set A".

n(A) **NUMBER OF ELEMENTS IN SET A** Instead of writing "There are 12 elements in set A" you can write n(A) = 12.

$\varnothing$ **THE EMPTY SET** If a set has <u>no elements</u> in it at all, it's called <u>the empty set</u>. E.g. if set B = {negative numbers between 1 and 10} then set B = $\varnothing$.

For the empty set, n(A) = 0

Collect similar things to make sets — this reminds me of Monopoly...

...except that it doesn't end with your brother trying to shove hotels up his nose. It ends with practice questions.

1) B = {x: x is a square number and x < 110}. List all the elements that are in set B. Use set notation to say that 22 is not an element of this set.

2) Come up with your own example of a set, and write a description of it using one of the methods shown above.

Sets

This page is all about how you can <u>describe</u> the ways that sets <u>relate to each other</u>.
There are a couple more symbols to learn, but don't worry — it's not as scary as it might look.

Venn Diagrams use Circles to Represent Sets

A Venn diagram is just a <u>visual way</u> of showing the <u>relationships between sets</u>. Here are the basics:

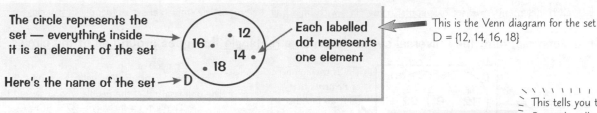

The circle represents the
set — everything inside
it is an element of the set

Each labelled
dot represents
one element

16 .   . 12
. 14
. 18
D

Here's the name of the set ➔ D

This is the Venn diagram for the set
D = {12, 14, 16, 18}

BUT lots of Venn diagrams <u>don't</u> have a labelled dot for each
element. They often have a number in each section instead
— it tells you <u>how many elements</u> there are in that section.

This tells you there are
3 people called Tim in
my class — so n(T) = 3.

T
3

T = {People called Tim in my class}

With More Than One set you get Unions and Intersections

When there's more than one set, things get more interesting — we're talking UNIONS and INTERSECTIONS.

1) The <u>UNION</u> of the sets: This is a <u>bigger set</u> containing <u>all the elements</u> that are in <u>either set</u>.
   In set notation, you can write it as A ∪ B

EXAMPLE: As part of a survey a group of people were asked if they own a cat or a dog.

If set C = {cat owners} and set D = {dog owners}, the <u>union</u> of the sets is all the people who
own <u>either a cat or a dog</u>. You can write this as C ∪ D = {people who own a cat or a dog}.

The green area of the
Venn diagram is the
<u>union</u> of the two sets.

C   D
12   6   22

So you can say that:
n(C ∪ D) = 12 + 6 + 22 = 40

12 people own just cats   6 people own cats and dogs   22 people own just dogs   n(C) = 18 and n(D) = 28

2) The <u>INTERSECTION</u> of the sets: This is a <u>smaller set</u> containing <u>only the elements</u> that are in <u>both sets</u>.
   You can write it in set notation like this: A ∩ B

The <u>intersection</u> of the two sets is all the people who own <u>both a cat and a dog</u>.
You can write this as C ∩ D = {people who own a cat and a dog}.

This time the green
area is the <u>intersection</u>
of the two sets.

C   D
12   6   22

So you can say that:
n(C ∩ D) = 6

But what if your set is a set of coloured circles...

For all the long words, 'union' is just 'things in either' and 'intersection' is 'things in both'.

1) The Venn diagram on the right shows two overlapping sets called set P and set Q.
   Find: a) set P   b) n(Q)   c) set (P ∪ Q)   d) set P ∩ Q   e) n(P ∩ Q)

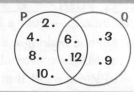

P   Q
. 2.
4.   . 6.   .3
8.   .12   .9
10.

Sets

We're on the home stretch now — it's the last page about <u>sets</u>, and the last page of the section.

The Universal Set contains every Possible Value

1) The UNIVERSAL SET is the group of things that you <u>select the elements</u> of your <u>set</u> from. It's represented by ξ.

> E.g. all the elements in a set of '<u>people in my class with blue hair</u>' belong to the universal set of '<u>people in my class</u>'.

2) On a Venn diagram, the universal set is shown as a <u>rectangle</u> that goes <u>around all of the circles</u>, like this:

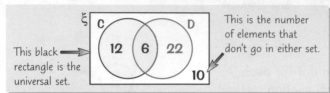

This black rectangle is the universal set.

This is the number of elements that don't go in either set.

This Venn diagram goes with the survey on page 11. The universal set is the people who answered the survey. That's 10 + 12 + 6 + 22 = 50 people. There must be 10 of them who don't own a cat or a dog.

3) The COMPLEMENT of a set is all the members of the <u>universal set</u> that <u>aren't</u> in the set. If the set is A, then its complement is written A'.

Set A = {odd integers between 0 and 10}
ξ = {integers between 0 and 10}
A = {1, 3, 5, 7, 9}
A' = {2, 4, 6, 8}

Subsets are Sets Within Sets

1) A SUBSET is a set that is entirely contained <u>within</u> another set.

2) This means that <u>all</u> the elements that are in the <u>first set</u> are <u>also in the second set</u>.

> E.g. if A = {5, 7, 11} and B = {prime numbers} then A is a subset of B (because 5, 7 and 11 are all prime numbers).

3) There's another handy symbol for this: $\subseteq$ **...IS A SUBSET OF...**
So rather than writing "set A is a subset of set B", you can write "A $\subseteq$ B"

4) And, of course, there's a symbol meaning the opposite too: $\not\subseteq$ **...IS NOT A SUBSET OF...**
E.g. if this time set A = {4, 8, 12} and set B = {prime numbers}, you can write "A $\not\subseteq$ B"

5) On a <u>Venn diagram</u> a circle that represents a subset will be drawn <u>inside</u> the larger circle that represents the main set — giving you something that looks like this:

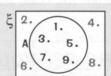

A Proper Subset has Fewer Elements than the Main Set

1) Most of the time the <u>subsets</u> you deal with will <u>contain fewer elements</u> than the main set. These are PROPER SUBSETS.

> E.g. if A = {2, 3, 4} and B = {1, 2, 3, 4, 5}, then A is a proper subset of B.

2) The symbol $\subset$ means "<u>...is a proper subset of...</u>". So you can just write "A $\subset$ B"

3) But you can have a set that contains <u>exactly the same</u> elements as your main set — the two sets might be <u>identical</u>. One still counts as a <u>subset</u> of the other, but <u>not</u> a proper subset.

> E.g. if A = {x, y, z} and B = {x, y, z} then A is not a proper subset of B.

4) The symbol $\not\subset$ means "<u>...is not a proper subset of...</u>". So you can write "A $\not\subset$ B"

{me, you} — a subset of people who are glad they're at the end of Section 1...

Well, nearly — just a few more practice questions, and that's it...

1) Mike is making a set using the rule {square numbers that are less than 20}. He writes S = {1, 4, 9, 16}.
   a) Mike's universal set is the natural numbers less than 20. What elements are in S'?
   b) Write a set that is a proper subset of S.

Revision Summary

Phew, that's the first section over with... Lots of important little bits of maths in there — so make sure you know it all really well. And, as if by magic, here's a page of revision questions to help you do just that. Use them to find out which bits you need to brush up on, and keep at it until you can do them all... (Handily, they follow the sequence of the pages, so you can easily look up anything you don't know.)

1) What are integers, natural numbers and real numbers?

2) Write out the first ten square numbers.

3) Name three different forms that a rational number can take, and give examples.

4) Explain the difference between rational and irrational numbers.

5) What are the steps of the method for determining if a number is prime?

6) Is 161 a prime number?

7) Find all the factors of 42.

8) Find the common factors of 24, 30 and 36.

9) Find the highest common factor of 28 and 63.

10) List the first 10 multiples of 13.

11) Find three common multiples of 12 and 18.

12) Find the lowest common multiple of 12 and 21.

13) Find all the possible values of:
   a) $\sqrt{256}$ b) $\sqrt[3]{216}$ c) $\sqrt{324}$

14) If $2 \times h^2 = 72$, find the two possible values of h.

15) Explain what BODMAS means.

16) Find the value of the following expression: $30 - (14 \div 7)^3 \times 3 + 11$

17) Write out the following sentence as a mathematical expression:
   "Add six to eleven, and multiply the result by five."

18) Using your calculator, convert 5¾ into a top-heavy fraction.

19) Anja is filling in some forms to show how much beer has been made at her brewery.
   The numbers must be entered in standard form. Write Anja's numbers in standard form:
   a) 970 000 cans   b)   6 830 000 bottles   c)   3 560 000 000 pints

20) Paul needs to set his machine to cut metal sheeting to a thickness of 2.75×10^{-6} m.
   The machine won't accept standard form. What number should Paul type in?

21) $Q = \{x: x \text{ is an integer and } 3 \leq x \leq 11\}$. List all of the elements that are in set Q.

22) Write the following using set notation:
   a) There are fifty elements in set W.   b) Set H is equal to the empty set.
   c) Cheddar is an element of set Z.   d) Set F is not a subset of set G.

23) Draw a Venn diagram to illustrate these two overlapping sets: set A = {1, 3, 5, 7, 9}
                                                                        set B = {5, 6, 7, 8, 9}
   Find set (A $\cup$ B), set (A $\cap$ B) and n(A $\cup$ B). Write out a proper subset of A, and call it C.

24) Kate asks everyone at her school if they like tea, coffee
   and limeade. She ends up with three sets: T = {like tea},
   C = {like coffee} and L = {like limeade}.
   The Venn diagram on the right shows her results.
   a) What is Kate's universal set? How many elements does it have?
   b) How many people like tea and limeade, but not coffee?
   c) Find n(T).
   d) Find n(L'). What does this number represent?
   e) Find n((C $\cap$ L) $\cup$ T')

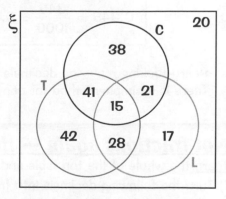

Section One — Numbers

Fractions, Decimals and Percentages

The one word that could describe all these three is <u>PROPORTION</u>. Fractions, decimals and percentages are simply <u>three different ways</u> of expressing a <u>proportion</u> of something — and it's pretty important you should see them as <u>closely related and completely interchangeable</u> with each other. This table shows the really common conversions which you should know straight off without having to work them out:

Fraction	Decimal	Percentage
$\frac{1}{2}$	0.5	50%
$\frac{1}{4}$	0.25	25%
$\frac{3}{4}$	0.75	75%
$\frac{1}{3}$	0.333333... or $0.\dot{3}$	$33\frac{1}{3}$%
$\frac{2}{3}$	0.666666... or $0.\dot{6}$	$66\frac{2}{3}$%
$\frac{1}{10}$	0.1	10%
$\frac{2}{10}$	0.2	20%
$\frac{X}{10}$	0.X	X0%
$\frac{1}{5}$	0.2	20%
$\frac{2}{5}$	0.4	40%

> A number with a dot over it means that the number repeats forever — see the next page.

The more of those conversions you learn, the better — but for those that you <u>don't know</u>, you must <u>also learn</u> how to <u>convert</u> between the three types. These are the methods:

$$\text{Fraction} \xrightarrow{\substack{\text{Divide (use your} \\ \text{calculator if you can)} \\ \text{e.g. } \frac{1}{2} \text{ is } 1 \div 2}} \text{Decimal} \xrightarrow{\substack{\times \text{ by 100}}} \text{Percentage}$$
$$= 0.5 \qquad \text{e.g. } 0.5 \times 100 \qquad = 50\%$$

$$\text{Fraction} \xleftarrow{\substack{\text{The awkward one}}} \text{Decimal} \xleftarrow{\substack{\div \text{ by 100}}} \text{Percentage}$$

<u>Converting decimals to fractions</u> is fairly easy to do when you have <u>exact</u> (terminating) decimals. It's best illustrated by examples — you should be able to work out the rule...

$$0.6 = \frac{6}{10} \qquad 0.3 = \frac{3}{10} \qquad 0.7 = \frac{7}{10} \qquad 0.x = \frac{x}{10} \text{ etc.}$$
$$0.12 = \frac{12}{100} \qquad 0.78 = \frac{78}{100} \qquad 0.45 = \frac{45}{100} \qquad 0.05 = \frac{5}{100} \text{ etc.}$$
$$0.345 = \frac{345}{1000} \qquad 0.908 = \frac{908}{1000} \qquad 0.024 = \frac{24}{1000} \qquad 0.xyz = \frac{xyz}{1000} \text{ etc.}$$

> These can then be <u>cancelled down</u> — see p.7

Scary-looking <u>recurring</u> decimals like 0.3333333 are actually just <u>exact fractions</u> in disguise. There is a simple method for converting them into fractions — see next page...

<u>Not fractions again — they're like a recurring nightmare...</u>

<u>Learn</u> the whole of the top table and the 4 conversion processes. Then it's time to break into a mild sweat...

1) Turn the following decimals into fractions and reduce them to their simplest form.

   a) 0.6   b) 0.02   c) 0.77   d) 0.555   e) 5.6

Fractions, Decimals and Percentages

You might think that a decimal is just a decimal. But oh no — things get a lot more juicy than that...

Recurring or Terminating...

1) <u>Recurring</u> decimals have a <u>pattern</u> of numbers which repeats forever, e.g. $\frac{1}{3}$ is the decimal 0.333333...
Note, it doesn't have to be a single digit that repeats. You could have, for instance: 0.143143143....

2) <u>Terminating</u> decimals are <u>finite</u>, e.g $\frac{1}{20}$ is the decimal 0.05.

3) You should have worked out from the previous page the easy method for converting <u>terminating decimals</u> into fractions — you basically just divide by a <u>power of 10</u> depending on the number of digits after the decimal point. Converting <u>recurring decimals</u> isn't much harder once you've learnt the method...

Recurring Decimals into Fractions

There's two ways to do it: 1) by <u>UNDERSTANDING</u>   2) by just <u>LEARNING THE RESULT</u>.

The Understanding Method:

1) Find the <u>length</u> of the <u>repeating sequence</u> and <u>multiply</u> by 10, 100, 1000, 10 000 or whatever to move it all up past the decimal point by <u>one full repeated lump</u>:
E.g. 0.234234234... × 1000 = 234.234234...

2) <u>Subtract the original number</u>, r, from the new one (which in this case is 1000r)
i.e. 1000r − r = 234.234234... − 0.234234... giving: 999r = 234

3) Then just <u>DIVIDE</u> to leave r: $r = \dfrac{234}{999}$, and cancel if possible: $r = \dfrac{26}{111}$

The 'Just Learning The Result' Method:

The fraction always has the repeating unit on the top and the same number of nines on the bottom — easy as that. Look at these and marvel at the elegant simplicity of it.

$$0.4444444... = \frac{4}{9} \qquad 0.34343434... = \frac{34}{99}$$

$$0.124124124... = \frac{124}{999} \qquad 0.14561456... = \frac{1456}{9999}$$

Always check if it will <u>CANCEL DOWN</u> of course, e.g. $0.363636... = \dfrac{36}{99} = \dfrac{4}{11}$.

Oh, what's recurrin'?...

Learn how to tell whether a fraction will be a <u>terminating or recurring decimal</u>, and all the <u>methods above</u>. Then turn over and write it all down. Now, try and answer these beauties...

1) Express 0.142857142857... as a fraction.

2) Without cheating, say if these fractions will give recurring or terminating decimals: a) $\dfrac{3}{8}$ b) $\dfrac{9}{280}$ c) $\dfrac{7}{250}$

Extended

Extended

Fractions

This page shows you how to cope with fraction calculations without your <u>beloved calculator</u>.

1) *Multiplying — easy*

Multiply top and bottom separately:

$$\frac{3}{5} \times \frac{4}{7} = \frac{3 \times 4}{5 \times 7} = \frac{12}{35}$$

2) *Dividing — quite easy*

Turn the 2nd fraction <u>UPSIDE DOWN</u> and then <u>multiply</u>:

$$\frac{3}{4} \div \frac{1}{3} = \frac{3}{4} \times \frac{3}{1} = \frac{3 \times 3}{4 \times 1} = \frac{9}{4}$$

3) *Adding, subtracting — fraught*

Add or subtract <u>TOP LINES ONLY</u> but <u>only</u> if the <u>bottom numbers</u> are the same. If they're not, you have to equalise the denominator first — see below.

$$\frac{2}{6} + \frac{1}{6} = \frac{3}{6} \qquad \frac{5}{7} - \frac{3}{7} = \frac{2}{7}$$

4) *Cancelling down — easy*

<u>Divide top and bottom by the same number</u>, till they won't go any further:

$$\overset{\div 3 \quad \div 2}{\frac{18}{24} = \frac{6}{8} = \frac{3}{4}}$$
$$\underset{\div 3 \quad \div 2}{}$$

5) *Finding a fraction of something — just multiply*

<u>Multiply</u> the 'something' by the <u>TOP</u> of the fraction, then <u>divide</u> it by the <u>BOTTOM</u>:

$$\frac{9}{20} \text{ of } \pounds 360 = (9 \times \pounds 360) \div 20 = \frac{\pounds 3240}{20} = \pounds 162$$

6) *Equalising the Denominator*

This comes in handy for ordering fractions by size, and for adding or subtracting fractions. You need to find a common multiple of all the denominators:

> Example: Put these fractions in ascending order of size: $\frac{8}{3}, \frac{6}{4}, \frac{12}{5}$
>
> Lowest Common Multiple of 3, 4 and 5 is 60 $\Longrightarrow$ $\frac{8}{3} = \frac{8}{3} \times \frac{20}{20} = \frac{160}{60}$
>
> so put all the fractions over 60... $\frac{6}{4} = \frac{6}{4} \times \frac{15}{15} = \frac{90}{60}$
>
> $\frac{12}{5} = \frac{12}{5} \times \frac{12}{12} = \frac{144}{60}$
>
> So the correct order is $\frac{90}{60}, \frac{144}{60}, \frac{160}{60}$ i.e. $\frac{6}{4}, \frac{12}{5}, \frac{8}{3}$

7) *Dealing with Mixed Numbers*

Always change <u>mixed numbers</u> (things like $3\frac{1}{3}$) to normal fractions before you calculate with them.

$$3\frac{2}{3} \times 7\frac{3}{4} = \frac{11}{3} \times \frac{31}{4} \overset{\nearrow 2 + (3 \times 3)}{\searrow 3 + (7 \times 4)}$$
$$= \frac{341}{12}$$

<u>No fractions were harmed in the making of this page...</u>

Try all of the following <u>without</u> a calculator.

1) a) $\frac{3}{8} \times \frac{5}{12}$ b) $\frac{4}{5} \div \frac{7}{8}$ c) $\frac{3}{4} + \frac{2}{5}$ d) $\frac{2}{5} - \frac{3}{8}$ e) $4\frac{1}{9} + 2\frac{2}{27}$ 2 a) Find $\frac{2}{5}$ of 550.   b) What's $\frac{7}{8}$ of £2?

Multiplying and Dividing Decimals

Decimals are a little trickier to multiply and divide without a calculator than whole numbers — so you'll just have to make sure you <u>learn</u> these rules.

Multiplying Decimals

1) To start with, <u>forget</u> about the decimal points and do the multiplication using <u>whole numbers</u>. (E.g. for 1.2 × 3.45 you'd do 12 × 345.)

2) Now <u>count</u> the total number of digits after the <u>decimal points</u> in the original numbers. (E.g. 1.2 and 3.45 — so that's 3 digits after the decimal point.)

3) Make the answer have the same number of decimal places.

EXAMPLE: "Work out 4.6 × 2.7"

1) Work out 46 × 27 using whichever method you prefer. It's 1242.

2) 4.6 × 2.7 has 2 digits after the decimal points

3) So the answer is <u>12.42</u>

$$
\begin{array}{r}
4\,6 \\
\times\ 2\,7 \\
\hline
3\,2\,2 \\
9\,2\,0 \\
\hline
1\,2\,4\,2
\end{array}
$$

This is 7 × 46
This is 20 × 46

Dividing with Decimals

When dividing <u>a decimal by a whole number</u>, just do it like a whole-number division — but put the decimal point in the answer <u>right above</u> the one in the question.

EXAMPLE: "What is 52.8 ÷ 3?"

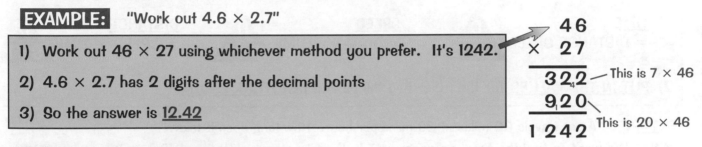

3 into 5 goes once, carry the remainder of 2.   3 into 22 goes 7 times, carry the remainder of 1.   3 into 18 goes 6 times exactly. So 52.8 ÷ 3 = 17.6.

When dividing <u>one decimal by another</u> your best bet is to turn it into a whole-number division:

EXAMPLE: "What is 83.6 ÷ 0.4?"

The trick with ones like this is to remember it's a fraction: $\dfrac{83.6}{0.4}$

Now you can get rid of the decimals by multiplying the top and bottom by 10 (turning it into an equivalent fraction): $\dfrac{83.6}{0.4} = \dfrac{836}{4}$

It's now a lovely decimal-free division that you know how to solve:

$$
\begin{array}{r}
2 \\
4\,|\,8\,3\,6
\end{array}
\quad\Rightarrow\quad
\begin{array}{r}
2\,0 \\
4\,|\,8\,3^{3}6
\end{array}
\quad\Rightarrow\quad
\begin{array}{r}
2\,0\,9 \\
4\,|\,8\,3^{3}6
\end{array}
\qquad \text{so } 83.6 \div 0.4 = 209.
$$

Decimal calculations — less painful than standing on a plug barefoot...

Hmm, lots of info to take in there — it's really important that you learn all the <u>methods</u> on this <u>page</u> though. Have another read if you're still a bit unsure. Then try all of these <u>without</u> a calculator:
1) 3.2 × 56   2) 0.6 × 10.2   3) 5.5 × 10.2
4) 33.6 ÷ 0.6   5) 69 ÷ 1.5   6) 43.2 ÷ 3.6

Speed, Distance and Time

Speed-distance-time questions are <u>very common</u>, and they never give you the formula.
Either you learn it beforehand or you wave goodbye to several easy marks.

1) The Formula Triangle

The formula triangle method is by far the best way to tackle speed-distance-time questions.

You have to <u>remember the order of the letters</u> in the triangle (SDT) — the word <u>SoDiT</u> might help.
So if it's a question on speed, distance and time just say: <u>SOD IT</u>.

Once you've got the formula triangle sorted out, the rest is easy:

1) <u>COVER UP the thing you want to find</u> and just <u>WRITE DOWN</u> what's left showing.

TIME
= DISTANCE/SPEED

SPEED
= DISTANCE/TIME

DISTANCE
= SPEED × TIME

2) <u>PUT IN THE VALUES</u> for the other two things and just <u>WORK IT OUT</u>.

<u>EXAMPLE</u>: "A car travels 90 miles at 36 miles per hour. How long does it take?"
<u>ANS</u>: We want to find the <u>time</u>, so <u>cover up T</u> in the triangle which leaves D/S,
so T = D/S = Distance ÷ speed = 90 ÷ 36 = <u>2.5 hours</u>

> You can use formula triangles for any formula of the type A = B × C or B = A ÷ C: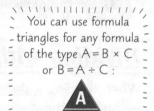

2) Units — Getting them right

By <u>units</u> we mean things like <u>cm, m, m/s, km²</u>, etc. and quite honestly they should always be in your mind
when you <u>write an answer down</u>. When you're using a FORMULA, there is one special thing you need to know.
It's simple enough but you must know it:

> The <u>UNITS you get out</u> of a Formula
> <u>DEPEND ENTIRELY</u> upon <u>the UNITS you put into it.</u>

For example, if you put a <u>distance in cm</u> and a <u>time in seconds</u> into the formula triangle to work
out SPEED, the answer must come out in <u>cm per second</u> (cm/s).

If the <u>time is in hours</u> and the speed in <u>kilometres per hour</u> (km/h) then the distance you
calculate will come out in <u>kilometres</u>. It's pretty simple when you think about it.

But Don't Mix Units

E.g. Don't mix <u>KILOMETRES Per HOUR</u> in a formula with a <u>time in MINUTES</u> (convert it to <u>hours</u>).

Example: "A boy walks 800 m in 10 minutes. Find his speed in km/h."
If you use 800 m and 10 minutes your answer will be a speed in <u>metres per minute</u> (m/min).
Instead you must <u>convert</u>: 800 m = <u>0.8 km</u>, 10 mins = <u>0.1667 hours</u> (mins÷60).
Then you can divide 0.8 <u>km</u> by 0.1667 <u>hours</u> to get <u>4.8 km/h</u>.

Together we shall rule the universe as finger and formula triangle...

Oh yes, it is your <u>destiny</u>. One step at a time though. First of all you need to learn this page, so turn over and
briefly summarise both topics, with examples. Keep trying until you can <u>remember it all</u>. Then as your big finale:

1) Find the time taken, in hours, mins and secs, for a purple-nosed buffalo walking at
   3.2 km/h to cover 5.2 km.
2) Also find how far it would go in 35 mins and 25 seconds. Give your answer in both km and m.

Ratios

The whole grisly subject of <u>RATIOS</u> gets a lot easier when you do this:

Treat RATIOS like FRACTIONS

So for the <u>RATIO</u> 3:4, you'd treat it as the <u>FRACTION</u> $\frac{3}{4}$, which is 0.75 as a <u>DECIMAL</u>.

What the fraction form of the ratio actually means

1) Suppose in a class there's <u>girls and boys</u> in the ratio 3 : 4.
   This means there's $\frac{3}{4}$ as many girls as boys.

2) So if there were 20 boys, there would be $\frac{3}{4} \times 20 = 15$ girls.
   You've got to be careful though — it <u>doesn't mean</u> $\frac{3}{4}$ of the <u>people</u> in the class are girls.

Reducing Ratios to their simplest form

You reduce ratios just like you'd reduce fractions to their simplest form.
For the ratio 15:18, both numbers have a <u>factor</u> of 3, so <u>divide them by 3</u> — that
gives 5:6. We can't reduce this any further. So the simplest form of 15:18 is <u>5 : 6</u>.

Treat them just like fractions — use your calculator if you can

Now this is really sneaky. If you stick in a fraction using the $a\frac{b}{c}$ button,
your calculator automatically cancels it down when you press $=$.
So for the ratio 8:12, just press 8 $a\frac{b}{c}$ 12 $=$, and you'll get the reduced fraction $\frac{2}{3}$.
Now you just change it back to ratio form ie. <u>2 : 3</u>. Ace.

The More Awkward Cases:

1) The $a\frac{b}{c}$ button will only accept whole numbers

So if the ratio is something like '2.4 : 3.6' or '1¼ : 3½' then you must...

MULTIPLY BOTH SIDES by the SAME NUMBER until they are both WHOLE NUMBERS

E.g. for '1¼ : 3½', multiplying both sides by 4 gives '<u>5 : 14</u>' (Try $a\frac{b}{c}$, but it won't cancel further.)

2) If the ratio is MIXED UNITS

CONVERT BOTH SIDES into the SMALLER UNITS using the relevant CONVERSION FACTOR (see P.24)

E.g. '24 mm : 7.2 cm' ($\times$ 7.2 cm by 10) $\Rightarrow$ 24 mm : 72 mm = <u>1 : 3</u> (using $a\frac{b}{c}$)

3) To reduce a ratio to the form 1 : n or n : 1 (n can be any number)

Simply DIVIDE BOTH SIDES BY THE SMALLEST SIDE.

This form is often the <u>most useful</u>, since it shows the ratio very clearly.

E.g. take "<u>3 : 56</u>" — dividing both sides by 3 gives: <u>1 : 18.7</u> (56÷3) (i.e. 1 : n)

Ratios

There's just so much <u>great stuff</u> to say about ratios. I couldn't possibly fit it onto only one page...

Using The Formula Triangle in Ratio Questions

EXAMPLE: "Mortar is made from sand and cement in the ratio 7:2. If 9 buckets of sand are used, how much cement is needed?"

This is a fairly common type of Exam question and it's pretty tricky for most people — but once you start using the formula triangle method (see p18), it's a bit of a breeze...

This is the basic **FORMULA TRIANGLE** for **RATIOS**, <u>but</u> **NOTE:**

$$\frac{A}{A{:}B \times B}$$

1) <u>THE RATIO MUST BE THE RIGHT WAY ROUND</u>, with the <u>FIRST NUMBER IN THE RATIO</u> relating to <u>the item ON TOP</u> in the triangle.

2) <u>You'll always need to CONVERT THE RATIO</u> into its <u>EQUIVALENT FRACTION</u> or Decimal to work out the answer.

1) Here's the formula triangle for the mortar question...

2) The trick is to replace the ratio 7:2 by its <u>EQUIVALENT FRACTION</u> — 7/2, or 3.5 as a decimal (7÷2).

3) So, <u>covering up cement in the triangle</u>, gives us 'cement = sand / (7:2)' i.e. '9 / 3.5' = 9 ÷ 3.5 = 2.57 or about <u>2½ buckets of cement</u>.

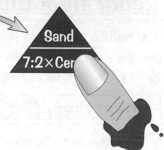

$$\frac{\text{Sand}}{7{:}2 \times \text{Cer}}$$

Proportional Division

In a <u>proportional division</u> question a <u>TOTAL AMOUNT</u> is to be <u>split in a certain ratio</u>.

EXAMPLE: "£9100 is to be split in the ratio 2:4:7. Find the 3 amounts."

The key word here is <u>PARTS</u> — concentrate on 'parts' and it all becomes quite painless:

1) <u>ADD UP THE PARTS</u>:
   The ratio 2:4:7 means there will be a total of 13 <u>parts</u>   i.e. 2+4+7 = <u>13 PARTS</u>

2) <u>FIND THE AMOUNT FOR ONE "PART"</u>
   Just divide the <u>total amount</u> by the number of <u>parts</u>: £9100 ÷ 13 = <u>£700</u> (= 1 PART)

3) <u>HENCE FIND THE THREE AMOUNTS</u>:
   2 parts = 2×700 = <u>£1400</u>,   4 parts = 4×700 = <u>£2800</u>,   7 parts = <u>£4900</u>

Ratio Nelson — didn't he proportionally divide the French at Trafalgar...

Oh I do make myself chuckle. Learn the <u>rules for simplifying</u>, the <u>formula triangle for ratios</u>, and the <u>3 steps for proportional division</u>. Now turn over and <u>write down</u> what you've learned. Then try these:

1) Simplify: a) 25:35   b) 3.4 : 5.1   c) 2¼ : 3¾
2) Porridge and ice-cream are mixed in the ratio 7:4.
   How much porridge should go with 10 bowls of ice-cream?
3) Divide £8400 in the ratio 5:3:4

Proportion

Sometimes you have two numbers that are <u>linked</u>. If one changes, the other changes too.

Directly Proportional Numbers Both Increase Together

1) Sometimes increasing one number means another number increases by the <u>same factor</u>.
   E.g. the <u>number of eggs</u> you need depends on <u>how many people</u> you're making omelettes for.
   This table shows how many eggs you need for different numbers of people.

2) If you <u>double</u> one value, you <u>double</u> the other, if you
   <u>times one of them by 5</u>, you <u>times the other by 5</u>, etc.

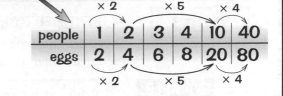

3) In cases like this, the pairs of numbers are in
   <u>DIRECT PROPORTION</u> to each other.

4) The <u>RATIO is the same for all pairs</u> of values, i.e.:

$$\frac{1}{2} = \frac{2}{4} = \frac{3}{6} = \frac{4}{8} = \frac{10}{20} = 0.5$$

This means direct proportion problems are just like <u>ratio</u> problems, so use the same method:

> **EXAMPLE:** "The height of a doo-dah tree is directly proportional to its number of leaves.
> If an 11 m tall doo-dah tree has 6 leaves, how tall will one with 14 leaves be?"
>
>
>
> 1) Make the formula triangle.
> 2) <u>Covering up 'Height'</u>, gives us 'height = (11:6) × leaves
>   i.e. '1.833 × 14 = <u>25.67 m tall</u>

Inverse Proportion — One Increases, One Decreases

1) Two numbers can also be <u>inversely proportional</u> to each other.
   Imagine you have £100 to share out equally. The <u>more people</u>
   it's shared between, the <u>less</u> each person gets.

people	1	2	4	5	10	100
£	100	50	25	20	10	1

2) If you <u>double</u> one value, you <u>halve</u> the other, if you
   <u>times one of them by 3</u>, you <u>divide the other by 3</u>, etc.

3) You need a bit of a different method to solve <u>inverse proportion problems</u>.
   The length of time a job takes with different numbers of people is an old favourite:

> **EXAMPLE:** "It takes 4 people 14 hours to paint a very big wall.
> How long would it have taken 7 people?"
>
> 1) Find the factor the number of people has <u>increased</u> by:
>
> | people | 4 | 7 |
> |--------|-----|-----|
> | hours | 14 | |
>
> 2) So the time required must have <u>decreased</u> by the same factor.
>
> | people | 4 | 7 |
> |--------|-----|-----|
> | hours | 14 | 8 |
>
> So, it'd have taken 7 people <u>8 hours</u>.

How long does it take to dig yourself into half a hole...

Well actually, you can't have half a hole. A hole is a hole. Anyway, enough philosophical debate. Try these:
1) A hairdresser charges an amount directly proportional to how long your hair is.
   Beth is charged £5.50 and her hair is 10 cm long. Sue's hair is 8 cm long. How much will Sue pay?
2) It takes 21 minutes to drive from A to B at 30 km/h. How long will it take to drive from A to B at 45 km/h?

Percentages

You shouldn't have any trouble with most percentage questions, especially types 1 and 2. Watch out for <u>type 3</u> questions and make sure you know the <u>proper method</u> for them.

| **Type 1** | "Find x% of y" — e.g. Find 15% of £46 $\Rightarrow$ 0.15 × 46 = <u>£6.90</u> |

| **Type 2** | "Express x as a percentage of y"
e.g. Give 40p as a percentage of £3.34 $\Rightarrow$ (40 ÷ 334) × 100 = <u>12%</u> |

| **Type 3** | — IDENTIFIED BY <u>NOT</u> GIVING THE "<u>ORIGINAL VALUE</u>" |

These are the type most people get wrong — but only because they don't recognise them as a type 3 and don't apply this simple method:

EXAMPLE:

A house increases in value by 20% to £72 000.
Find what it was worth <u>before</u> the rise.

METHOD:

$$÷120 \begin{cases} £72\,000 = 120\% \\ £600 = 1\% \end{cases}$$
$$×100 \begin{cases} £600 = 1\% \\ £60\,000 = 100\% \end{cases}$$

So the original price was <u>£60 000</u>

An <u>INCREASE</u> of 20% means that £72 000 represents <u>120%</u> <u>of the original</u> value. If it was a DROP of 20%, then we would put '£72 000 = <u>80%</u>' instead, and then divide by 80 on the LHS, instead of 120.

Always set them out <u>exactly like this example</u>. The trickiest bit is deciding the top % figure on the RHS — the 2nd and 3rd rows are <u>always</u> 1% and 100%.

Percentage Change

It is common to give a <u>change in value</u> as a <u>percentage</u>.
This is the formula for doing so — <u>LEARN IT, AND USE IT</u>:

$$\text{PERCENTAGE 'CHANGE'} = \frac{\text{'CHANGE'}}{\text{ORIGINAL}} \times 100$$

Use it, or lose it.

By 'change', we could mean all sorts of things such as: 'Profit', 'loss', 'appreciation', 'depreciation', 'increase', 'decrease', 'error', 'discount', etc. For example,

$$\text{percentage 'profit'} = \frac{\text{'profit'}}{\text{original}} \times 100$$

Note the great importance of using the <u>ORIGINAL VALUE</u> in this formula.

Example — Depreciation

David bought a new car last year for £11 995. By the end of the year, the car was worth £7400. Find the <u>percentage depreciation</u> in the value of the car over the first year.

"<u>Depreciation</u>" means a <u>decrease in value</u>, so this is just a <u>percentage decrease</u> question.

$$\text{% depreciation} = \frac{\text{depreciation}}{\text{original}} \times 100 = \frac{11\,995 - 7400}{11\,995} \times 100 = \underline{38.3\%}$$

Fact — 70% of people understand percentages, the other 40% don't...

Learn the details for the different types of <u>percentage question</u>, then <u>turn over</u> and <u>write it all down</u>.
1) A trader buys watches for £5 and sells them for £7. Find his profit as a percentage.
2) A car depreciates by 30% to £14 350. What was it worth before?

Time

You see <u>24 hour clocks</u> in lots of places so hopefully you're an expert in how to read them. The only thing you might need reminding about is 'am' and 'pm' in the <u>12 hour clock</u>:

`20:23:47`

`08:23:47`

1) am and pm

'am' means '<u>morning</u>'. It runs <u>from 12 midnight to 12 noon</u>.
'pm' means '<u>afternoon</u> and <u>evening</u>'. It runs <u>from 12 noon to 12 midnight</u>.

(though I guess you know that already)

2) Conversions

You'll definitely need to know these very important facts:

1 day = 24 hours
1 hour = 60 minutes
1 minute = 60 seconds

3) Exam questions involving 'time'

There are lots of different questions they can ask involving time but the same <u>GOOD OLD RELIABLE DEPENDABLE METHOD</u> will work wonders on all of them.

"And what is this good old reliable dependable method?", I hear you cry. Well, it's this:

> <u>Take your time</u>, <u>write it down</u>, and <u>split it up</u> into **SHORT EASY STAGES**

EXAMPLE: Find the time taken by a train which sets off at 1325 and arrives at 1910.

<u>WHAT YOU DON'T DO</u> is try to work it all out in your head <u>in one go</u> — this method <u>fails nearly every time</u>. Instead, split it into <u>short easy stages</u> like this:

1325　　→　　1400　　→　　1900　　→　　1910
　　35 mins　　　5 hours　　　10 mins

This is a nice safe way of finding the total time from 1325 to 1910:
5 hours + 35 mins + 10 mins = <u>5 hours 45 mins</u>.

4) If you use your Calculator, beware...

Try to avoid using the calculator with time measurements — it's a pain in the neck.
You'll get answers in decimals, and you have to convert them into hours and minutes.
So <u>learn this example</u>:

> 2.5 hours = 2 ½ hours = 2 hours and 30 minutes

That sound right?
Of course it does.

<u>SO DON'T GO WRITING ANYTHING STUPID</u>, like:

> 2.5 hours = 2 hours and 50 minutes

← WRONG WRONG WRONG WRONG!!

BREAKING NEWS: Public panic after warning over calculator use...

You probably know lots of this stuff already. The tips are <u>useful</u> though — so don't just ignore them.

1) What is 1715 in 12 hour clock? (don't forget am/pm)
2) A plane sets off at 10.15 am. The flight lasts 5 hrs 50 mins. What is the arrival time?
3) How many minutes are there in a day? And how many seconds are there in a day?
4) What is 3.5 hours in hours and minutes? What is 5¾ hours in hours and minutes?

Measures

Conversion factors are a mighty powerful tool for dealing with a wide variety of questions. And what's more the method is _real easy_. Learn it now. It's ace.

> 1) Decide what the Conversion Factor is
>
> 2) Multiply by it AND divide by it
>
> 3) Choose the common sense answer

Time — an Important Example

"Convert 2.55 hours into minutes." — (N.B. This is NOT 2hrs 55mins)

1) Conversion factor = 60   — (simply because 1 hour = 60 mins)

2) 2.55 hrs × 60 = 153 mins (makes sense)
   2.55 hrs ÷ 60 = 0.0425 mins (ridiculous answer!)

3) So plainly the answer is that 2.55hrs = 153 mins

Units of Measure

There's loads of units of measure. Like the pico-parsec, which is about 30.8 kilometres. You don't need to know that one, but you do need to know these:

1) Length   mm, cm, m, km
2) Area mm^2, cm^2, m^2, km^2,
3) Volume/Capacity mm^3, cm^3, m^3, ml, litres
4) Weight   g, kg, tonnes
5) Speed   km/h, m/s

> **MEMORISE THESE KEY FACTS:**
> 1 cm = 10 mm   1 tonne = 1000 kg
> 1 m = 100 cm   1 litre = 1000 ml
> 1 km = 1000 m   1 litre = 1000 cm^3
> 1 kg = 1000 g   1 cm^3 = 1 ml

Converting from one unit of measure to another isn't too hard — as long as you know the conversion factor.

Just use the same three-step method. E.g.

"Convert 3.78 metres into centimetres."

1) Conversion factor = 100   — (simply because 1 m = 100 cm)

2) 3.78 m × 100 = 378 cm (makes sense)
   3.78 m ÷ 100 = 0.0378 cm (ridiculous answer!)

3) So plainly the answer is that 3.78 m = 378 cm

I didn't see any conversion factor. For me it was just a bit karaoke...

That's right, you're never going to be a pop star, so instead learn the 3 steps of the C.F. method, and try these:

1) Convert 431 minutes into hours.

2) Convert 2.3 km into m.

3) Convert 20000 mm into m.

Maps and Scale Drawings

If maps were the same size as the place they were showing, then they'd be big... and a bit pointless. Thankfully maps are usually made using <u>scales</u>. The most usual map scale is '<u>1 cm = so many km</u>'. This just tells you <u>how many km in real life</u> it is for <u>1 cm measured on the actual map itself</u>.

1) Converting 'cm on a Map' into 'Real km'

This map shows the original Roman M6 Motorway built by the Emperor Hadrian in the year AD120.

Example:

> The scale of the map is '1 cm to 12 000 m'
> "Work out the length of the section of M6 between Wigan and Preston."

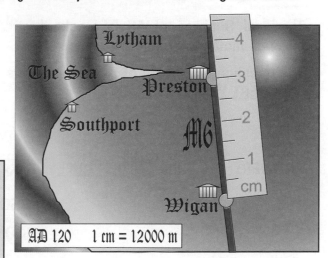

AD 120   1 cm = 12 000 m

This is what you do:

1) <u>MEASURE</u> the distance on the map.

   The distance is 3 cm.

2) Use the 3-step <u>CONVERSION FACTOR METHOD</u> from the previous page to convert the distance.

   • Conversion Factor = 12 000

   • 3 cm × 12 000 = 36 000 m (looks OK)
     3 cm ÷ 12 000 = 0.00025 m (not good)

   • So <u>36 000 m</u> (or 36 km) is the answer.

Picture of 80's mobile.
Scale: 1 cm = 3.6 km

2) Converting 'Real m' into 'cm on a drawing'

Instead of a map, you might get a question about a <u>plan</u> in your exam — like a plan of someone's <u>bedroom</u> or a <u>garden</u>. You do them in just the <u>same way</u> — the only difference is that the <u>scale</u> will probably be in <u>m</u> rather than <u>km</u>, e.g. 1 cm to 2 m (1:200).

Example:

> "A plan of a garden is being drawn at a scale of 1:50. If the patio is 4 metres wide, how wide should it be drawn on the plan?"

A scale of 1:50 means both units are the same. So it's 1 cm to 50 cm, or 1 m to 50 m.

Answer:

Use the 3-step <u>CONVERSION FACTOR METHOD</u> again:

• Conversion Factor = 50

• 4 m × 50 = 200 m (not good — bigger than in real life)
  4 m ÷ 50 = 0.08 m (looks OK)

• So <u>0.08 m</u> (or 8 cm) is the answer.

You might even be asked to <u>draw</u> something on a plan — just use the <u>method above</u> to work out how <u>big</u> it should be on the plan, then draw it.

Money Questions

A favourite type of question they like to ask you in Exams is comparing the 'value for money' of 2 or 3 similar items. Always follow the GOLDEN RULE...

Divide by the PRICE in pence (to get the amount per penny)

Example:

The local 'Supplies 'n' Vittals' stocks three sizes of Jamaican Gooseberry Jam.

The question is: Which of these represents 'THE BEST VALUE FOR MONEY'?

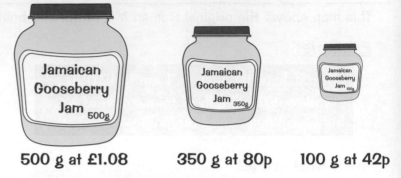

500 g at £1.08   350 g at 80p   100 g at 42p

ANSWER: Using the GOLDEN RULE:

500 g ÷ 108p	= 4.6 g PER PENNY
350 g ÷ 80p	= 4.4 g PER PENNY
100 g ÷ 42p	= 2.4 g PER PENNY

So you can now see straight away that THE 500 g JAR is the best value for money because you get MORE JAM PER PENNY. (As you should expect, it being the big jar).

With any question comparing 'value for money', DIVIDE BY THE PRICE (in pence) and it will always be the BIGGEST ANSWER is the BEST VALUE FOR MONEY.

Another Important Money Question — Converting Currency

If you're asked to convert from one currency to another, just use the conversion factor method from p24.

Here it is again to remind you...

1) Find the Conversion Factor
2) Multiply by it AND divide by it
3) Choose the common sense answer

"If £1 = 1.7 US Dollars, how much is 63 US dollars in £s?"

1) Obviously, conversion factor = 1.7 (The "exchange rate")
2) 63 × 1.7 = £107.10
   63 ÷ 1.7 = £37.06
3) Not quite so obvious this time, but since 1.7 US dollars = £1, you're clearly going to have fewer pounds than you had dollars (roughly half). So the answer has to be less than 63, which means it must be £37.06

The other golden rule — never dunk a biscuit for longer than 3 seconds...

Learn the Golden Rule for finding a best buy, and how to convert currency, then cover the page up and answer these little beauties:

1) Froggatt's 'Slugtail Soup' comes in three different sizes:
   The 150 g tin at 87p, the 250 g tin at £1.37 and the Farmhouse Size, 750 g at £3.95.
   Work out which one is the best value for money. (And don't just guess!)
2) Which is more, £34 or €45 ? (Exchange rate: £1 = €1.4)

Interest

When you leave money in a bank account, the bank pays you interest on it at a <u>percentage rate</u>.
The interest might be <u>compound or simple</u> — and you have to calculate both types...

Compound Interest — Interest is Added on Each Year

The amount you invest in an account is called the principal. Compound interest is added
on to the principal each year — so you get more and more interest each year.
Example:

"Ali invests £800 in an account that pays 2% compound interest each year. Find the amount in Ali's account after 3 years."

Value after 1 year:	£800 × 0.02 = £16 + 800 = £816
Value after 2 years:	£816 × 0.02 = £16.32 + 800 = £832.32
Value after 3 years:	£832.32 × 0.02 = £16.65 + 800 = <u>£848.97</u>

You can calculate compound interest using the <u>formula</u> for <u>compound growth and decay</u>:

Amount after n days/hours/years

$$N = P\left(1 + \frac{r}{100}\right)^n$$

Percentage change per day/hour/year

Number of days/hours/years

Initial amount

In the <u>example above</u>, P = £800, r = 2 and n = 3, so N = 800(1 + 0.02)³ = <u>£848.97</u>.

This formula can also be used when something is <u>decreasing in value</u> — in that case <u>r is negative</u>.
E.g. if a new car costs £11000 and decreases in value at a rate of 5% per year, after 4 years it
will have a value of 11000(1 – 0.05)⁴ = £8959.57.

Simple Interest is Different — It's a Bit Simpler...

In simple interest the value increases by the SAME AMOUNT OF MONEY each year.

E.g. "A man invests £1000 in a savings account which pays 8% SIMPLE interest per year. How much will there be after 6 years?"

Amount paid in interest each year:
£1000 × 8% = £1000 × 0.08 = £80

Multiply by the number of years: £80 × 6 = £480.

Add the interest and the initial amount together:
£1000 + £480 = <u>£1480</u>

You Might Have to Work Out the Amount Invested

In an Exam, you might be told how much is in an account at the end of the year, and the rate of interest, and
asked to work out the principal. These are Type 3 percentage questions — see p22.

E.g. "Glenn invested some money in an account that pays 4% interest per year. After the interest is added at the end of the year, there was £374.40. How much did Glenn invest?"

£374.40 = 104%
÷104
£3.60 = 1%
×100
£360 = 100%

So <u>£360</u> was invested.

Interest of 4% means that £374.40 represents <u>104% of the principal</u>.

You need to find the principal, which is 100% — so divide, then multiply.

I used to be a banker — but I lost interest...

Remember — always check whether the question is asking you for the principal, the interest, or the final amount.

1) Jo puts £100 in an account which pays 3% interest per year. How much will be in the account after 4 years
   a) if the bank pays simple interest?   b) if it's compound interest?
2) There's £2120 in an account after 1 year. If the account pays 6% interest, what was the principal?

Household Finance

Even if you plan to never leave your house again after your exams, you're still going to have to do some <u>calculations</u> — there's no escaping from Maths.

You Can Work Out Bills With Simple Calculations...

You may need to use your knowledge of percentages to answer questions on <u>bills</u>.

EXAMPLE: "Find the total cost of the electricity including **VAT** from the bill given below."

Previous meter reading	1654
New meter reading	2148
Price per unit (in pence)	12.5
Service Charge	£22.50
VAT at 5% of total charge	

ANSWER: Go through the bill step by step.

1) Find the <u>number of units</u> used (the difference):
2148 – 1654 = <u>494</u>

2) Multiply the <u>number of units</u> by the <u>price per unit</u>: 494 × 12.5 = 6175p = <u>£61.75</u>

3) Add the <u>service charge</u>: 61.75 + 22.50 = <u>£84.25</u>

4) Work out the VAT (see p.22) and <u>add it</u> to the total to get the final bill:
5% of £84.25 = 0.05 × 84.25 = £4.21. So the <u>total cost</u> is: 84.25 + 4.21 = <u>£88.46</u>

Tax Usually Has to be Paid on Earnings

If your earnings are over a certain amount, you have to pay <u>tax</u> on them.
Tax is paid at a percentage rate, but there are usually <u>different bands</u> to complicate things.

E.g. "Mike earns £35 000 a year. How much tax must he pay?"

ANSWER: First <u>split up</u> Mike's earnings into the different tax bands:
£2,000 at 0%.
£30 000 at 20%. This covers the first £32 000.
Then, £35 000 – £32 000 = £3000 at 40%

	Tax rate
The first £2000	0%
The next £30 000	20%
The rest of the earnings	40%

Now calculate the tax for each band:
20% of £30 000 = 0.2 × 30 000 = £6000
40% of £3000 = 0.4 × 3000 = £1200

So, the <u>total tax</u> is £6000 + £1200 = <u>£7200</u>

A Hire Purchase Includes a Deposit and Monthly Payments

You can sometimes buy things on <u>hire purchase</u>. This means you pay an <u>initial deposit</u> and then make <u>regular payments</u> over a set period of time.

E.g. "The cash price of a car is £12 000. It can be bought on hire purchase for a 15% deposit and 36 monthly payments of £320. What is the hire purchase price?"

ANSWER: Deposit: 0.15 × 12 000 = £1800. Monthly payments: 320 × 36 = £11 520

So the hire purchase price is: £1800 + £11 520 = <u>£13 320</u>

These finance questions can get a bit taxing...

There are loads of different types of household finance questions they could give you — don't panic if you get one you've never seen before. Read it carefully, and work out what exactly they're asking you to calculate. Percentages are likely to be involved — so try this one:

1) In the example above, what percentage of Mike's earnings does he pay in taxes? Answer to the nearest 1%.

Rounding Numbers

There are <u>two different ways</u> of specifying <u>where</u> a number should be <u>rounded off</u>.
They are: 'Decimal Places' and 'Significant Figures'.
Whichever way is used, the basic method is always the same and is shown below:

The Basic Method Has Three Steps

1) <u>Identify</u> the position of the LAST DIGIT.

2) Then look at the next digit to the RIGHT — called the DECIDER.

3) If the DECIDER is <u>5 or more</u>, then ROUND-UP the LAST DIGIT.
   If the DECIDER is <u>4 or less</u>, then leave the LAST DIGIT as it is.

EXAMPLE: "What is 7.45839 to 2 Decimal Places?"

$$7.45839 \quad = 7.46$$

<u>LAST DIGIT</u> to be written
(2nd decimal place because
we're rounding to 2 d.p.)

<u>DECIDER</u>

The <u>LAST DIGIT</u> rounds <u>UP</u>
because the <u>DECIDER</u>
is <u>5 or more</u>.

Decimal Places (D.P.)

This is pretty easy:

1) To round off to, say, <u>4 decimal places</u>,
   the <u>LAST DIGIT</u> will be the <u>4th one after the decimal point</u>.

2) There must be <u>no more digits</u> after the last digit (not even zeros).

EXAMPLE: Original number: <u>45.319461</u>

Rounded to 5 decimal places (5 d.p.)	45.31946	(DECIDER was 1, so <u>don't</u> round up)
Rounded to 4 decimal places (4 d.p.)	45.3195	(DECIDER was 6, so <u>do</u> round up)
Rounded to 3 decimal places (3 d.p.)	45.319	(DECIDER was 4, so <u>don't</u> round up)
Rounded to 2 decimal places (2 d.p.)	45.32	(DECIDER was 9, so <u>do</u> round up)

It's official — this is the most exciting page of revision ever...

OK, so I might have exaggerated a little. Still, it's proper important stuff, so you've got to stay awake long
enough to learn the <u>3 steps of the basic method</u> and the <u>2 extra points</u> for decimal places.
Now <u>turn over</u> and <u>write down what you've learned</u>. Then try again till you know it, and have a crack at these:
1) Round 3.5743 to 2 decimal places.   2) Give 0.0481 to 2 decimal places.
3) Express 12.9096 to 3 d.p.   4) Express 3546.054 to 1 d.p.

Rounding Numbers

Obviously all numbers are significant, but when it comes to <u>rounding</u>, some are more significant than others...

Significant Figures (S.F.)

The method for significant figures is <u>identical</u> to that for decimal places except that finding the <u>position</u> of the <u>LAST DIGIT</u> is more difficult — <u>it wouldn't be so bad, but for the ZEROS</u>...

1) The <u>1st significant figure</u> of any number is simply THE FIRST DIGIT WHICH ISN'T A ZERO.

2) The <u>2nd, 3rd, 4th</u>, etc. significant figures follow on immediately after the 1st, REGARDLESS OF BEING ZEROS OR NOT ZEROS.

E.g   **0.002309**   **2.03070**

<u>SIG FIGS</u>:   1st 2nd 3rd 4th   1st 2nd 3rd 4th

(If we're rounding to say, 3 s.f., then the LAST DIGIT is simply the 3rd sig. fig.)

3) After <u>Rounding Off</u> the LAST DIGIT, <u>end ZEROS</u> must be filled in <u>up to, BUT NOT BEYOND</u>, the decimal point.

No <u>extra zeros</u> must ever be put in <u>after</u> the decimal point.

Examples	to 4 s.f.	to 3 s.f.	to 2 s.f.	to 1 s.f.
1) 54.7651	54.77	54.8	55	50
2) 17.0067	17.01	17.0	17	20
3) 0.0045902	0.004590	0.00459	0.0046	0.005
4) 30895.4	30900	30900	31000	30000

Appropriate Accuracy

To decide what is appropriate accuracy, you need only remember these three rules:

1) For fairly <u>CASUAL MEASUREMENTS</u>, <u>2 SIGNIFICANT FIGURES</u> is most appropriate.

E.g. Cooking — 250 g (2 s.f.) of sugar, not 253 g (3 s.f.), or 300 g (1 s.f.)
Distance of a journey — 450 kilometres or 25 kilometres or 3500 kilometres (all 2 s.f.)
Area of a garden or floor — 330 m² or 15 m²

2) For more <u>IMPORTANT OR TECHNICAL THINGS</u>, <u>3 SIGNIFICANT FIGURES</u> is essential.

E.g. <u>A technical figure</u> like <u>34.2</u> metres per second, rather than 34 metres per second
A length that is <u>cut to fit</u>, e.g. measure a shelf <u>25.6 cm</u> long not just 26 cm
Any <u>accurate</u> measurement with a ruler: <u>67.5 cm</u> not 70 cm or 67.54 cm

3) Only for <u>REALLY SCIENTIFIC WORK</u> would you have <u>more than 3 SIG FIG</u>.

A bit of inappropriate humour — 5 significant figures walk into a bar...

<u>Learn the whole of this page</u>, then turn over and <u>write down everything you've learned</u>. And for pudding...

1) Round these to 2 d.p. :   a) 3.408   b) 1.051   c) 0.068   d) 3.596

2) Round these to 3 s.f. :   a) 567.78   b) 23445   c) 0.04563   d) 0.90876

3) Decide which category of accuracy these should belong in and round them off accordingly:
a) A jar of jam weighs 34.56 g   b) A car's max speed is 134.25 km/h   c) A cake needs 852.3 g of flour

Estimating

This is <u>VERY EASY</u>, so long as you don't <u>over-complicate it</u>.

Calculations

You should really do this every time you work something out on your <u>calculator</u>. It guards against daft mistakes that'd make you look like a prize plonker — see p7.

> 1) <u>ROUND EVERYTHING OFF</u> to nice easy <u>CONVENIENT NUMBERS</u>.
> 2) Then <u>WORK OUT THE ANSWER</u> using these nice easy numbers — that's it!

<u>EXAMPLE</u>: Estimate the value of $\dfrac{127.8 + 41.9}{56.5 \times 3.2}$ showing all your working.

<u>ANSWER</u>: $\dfrac{127.8 + 41.9}{56.5 \times 3.2} \approx \dfrac{130 + 40}{60 \times 3} = \dfrac{170}{180} \approx 1$

In the Exam you'll need to <u>show all the steps</u>, to prove you didn't just use a calculator.

Areas and Volumes

> 1) Draw or imagine a <u>RECTANGLE OR CUBOID</u> of similar size to the object.
> 2) <u>ROUND OFF</u> all lengths to the <u>NEAREST WHOLE</u>, and work it out — easy.

<u>EXAMPLES</u>: "Estimate the area of this shape and the volume of the bottle:"

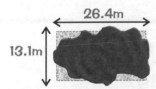

26.4m
13.1m

Area ≈ rectangle
26 m × 13 m = <u>338 m²</u>
(or without a calculator:
30 × 10 = 300 m²)

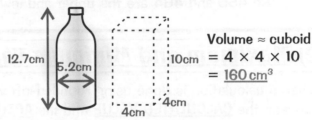

12.7cm   5.2cm

10cm
4cm   4cm

Volume ≈ cuboid
= 4 × 4 × 10
= <u>160 cm³</u>

Square Roots

> 1) Find the <u>TWO SQUARE NUMBERS EITHER SIDE</u> of the number in question.
> 2) Find the <u>SQUARE ROOTS</u> and pick a <u>SENSIBLE NUMBER IN BETWEEN</u>.

<u>EXAMPLE</u>: "Estimate $\sqrt{85}$ without using a calculator."

① The square numbers either side of 85 are <u>81</u> and <u>100</u>.

② The square roots are 9 and 10, so $\sqrt{85}$ must be <u>between 9 and 10</u>.
But 85 is much nearer 81 than 100, so $\sqrt{85}$ must be much <u>nearer 9 than 10</u>.
So pick <u>9.1, 9.2 or 9.3</u>. (The answer's actually 9.2195... if you're interested.)

The area of a splodge — just round it off to a rectangle. Hmmm...

LEARN the <u>rules for estimating</u>. Then <u>turn over and write them down</u>.
1) Estimate the volume of a tin of beans in cm³.
2) Without your calculator, estimate: a) $\sqrt{12}$, b) $\sqrt{104}$, c) $\sqrt{52}$, d) $\sqrt{30}$.

Accuracy and Measuring

No matter how accurately you measure something, you're always going to be a teensy bit out. It usually doesn't matter in the slightest for real-life, but it does for your Maths exam.

1) Upper and Lower bounds of a Measurement

The simple rule is this:

> The real value can be as much as HALF THE ROUNDED UNIT above and below the rounded-off value.

1) A room is given as being '9 m long to the nearest METRE' — its actual length could be anything from 8.5 m up to 9.5 m — i.e. HALF A METRE either side of 9 m. So 8.5m and 9.5m are the lower and upper bounds.

2) If it was given as '9.4 m, to the nearest 0.2 m', then it could be anything from 9.3 m up to 9.5 m (9.4 m ± 0.1 m) — i.e. 0.1 m either side of 9.4 m. So 9.3 m and 9.5 m are the lower and upper bounds.

3) If a length is given as 2.4 m to the nearest 0.1 m, the rounded unit is 0.1 m so the real value could be anything up to 2.4 m ± 0.05 m giving answers of 2.45 m and 2.35 m for the upper and lower bounds.

4) 'A school has 460 pupils to 2 Sig Fig' (i.e. to the nearest 10) — the actual figure could be anything from 455 up to 464. — (Why isn't it 465?) So 455 and 464 are the upper and lower bounds.

2) Maximum and Minimum Values for Calculations

Extended

When a calculation is done using rounded-off values there will be a DISCREPANCY between the CALCULATED VALUE and the ACTUAL VALUE:

EXAMPLE: A floor is measured as being 5.3 m × 4.2 m to the nearest 10 cm.

Calculate the minimum and maximum values for the area and perimeter.

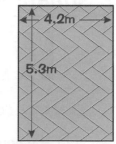

Multiplying 5.3 m by 4.2 m gives an area of 22.26 m², but this is not the actual floor area because the real length and width values could be anything from 5.25 m to 5.35 m and 4.15 m to 4.25 m,

∴ Maximum possible floor area = 5.35 × 4.25 = 22.7375 m²,

∴ Minimum possible floor area = 5.25 × 4.15 = 21.7875 m².

Also, using these values:

Maximum possible perimeter = (5.35 + 4.25) × 2 = 19.2 m,

Minimum possible floor area = (5.25 + 4.15) × 2 = 18.8 m.

Boundless enthusiasm — hope yours isn't wearing out yet...

Learn all the bits and bobs on this page then turn over and see how much you can remember. Try these too:

1) A yacht is described as 17 metres long to the nearest 0.1 m. What is the longest and shortest it could be?

2) x and y are measured as 2.32 m and 0.45 m to the nearest 0.01 m.
   a) Find the upper and lower bounds of x and y.
   b) If $z = x + 1/y$, find the max and min possible values of z.

Careful here — the biggest input values don't always give the biggest result.

Revision Summary

Section Two has been a pretty bumpy road — from fractions to estimation, via sticky topics such as ratio and percentages. Anyway, it's time to check what you can do as a result of bouncing over all these bumps — and there's a set of questions here to do just that. So give them a try, and if you come unstuck on any, give the relevant page another read-through.

1) Convert 0.645 into a <u>fraction</u>.

2) Demonstrate the 2 methods for converting recurring decimals to fractions.

3) Calculate a) 4/7 of 560   b) 2/5 of £150   c) 65% of 300

4) Work out <u>without</u> a calculator: a) $\frac{4}{6} \times 2\frac{12}{5}$ b) $\frac{25}{6} \div \frac{8}{3}$ c) $\frac{5}{8} + \frac{9}{4}$ d) $\frac{2}{3} - \frac{1}{7}$

5) Work out <u>without</u> a calculator: a) 12.1 × 0.8   b) 2.3 × 5.9   c) 24.6 ÷ 6   d) 37.5 ÷ 2.5

6) What are the 2 steps for using a formula triangle?

7) What is the formula triangle for speed, distance and time?

8) What two main rules apply to the units involved with formula triangles?

9) Sarah is in charge of ordering new stock for a clothes shop. The shop usually sells red scarves and blue scarves in the ratio 5:8. Sarah orders 150 red scarves. How many blue scarves should she order?

10) What are the three steps of the method of proportional division?

11) Jill, Heather and Susie spent Saturday helping out in their mum's cafe. Jill worked for 3 hours, Heather worked the next 2.5 hours and Susie worked for the final 1.5 hours of the day. They were given £42 to split between them for the work they'd done. How much should each of them receive?

12) Write down 3 pairs of numbers that show direct proportion, and 3 pairs that show inverse proportion.

13) Do your own example to illustrate each of the three types of percentage question.

14) Martin is trying to sell his car. He paid £5300 for it two years ago and is advised to sell it for 30% less than this original value. What price should he sell the car for?

15) A DVD player costs <u>£50 plus VAT</u>. If <u>VAT is 17.5%</u>, how much does the DVD player cost?

16) Carl has £35 to spend. He wants to use a <u>20%-off voucher</u> to buy a top that should cost £45. Can he afford the top?

17) Jo wants to eat dinner at 7.30pm. The meal takes 1 hour 20 minutes to prepare and 50 minutes to cook. What is the latest time she can start preparing it?

18) Convert 636 minutes into hours.

19) Give 8 metric conversions.

20) What is <u>The Golden Rule</u> for finding the 'Best Buy'?

21) Charley loves ham. Two different sized tins of Froggatt's Ham are on sale in his local shop. Which one is the 'Best Buy' for Charley?

22) Kylie is on holiday in South Africa, where £1 = 12.12 rand. She pays 250 rand to go to a safari park. How much has she spent in pounds?

23) Tim opens a savings account that pays 7% compound interest per year. He puts £100 into the account. How much will he have after 5 years to the nearest penny?

24) Jenny and two of her friends went out for dinner. The bill came to £51.98 and they decided to split it equally. How much, to two decimal places, should each of them pay?

25) Estimate the following square roots: $\sqrt{14}$, $\sqrt{70}$, $\sqrt{32}$, $\sqrt{35}$

26) How do you determine the upper and lower bounds of a rounded measurement?

27) A field has a length of 56 m and a width of 22 m, measured to the nearest metre.
   a) What are the upper and lower bounds of these measurements?
   b) Calculate the minimum and maximum areas of the field.

Conversion Graphs and Gradients

Here we go with section three then — kicking off with a couple of pages about what you can use graphs for.

Conversion Graphs — How to Get Answers from them

Conversion Graphs are really easy to use. They're just a quick way of converting between things like £ → Dollars or mph → km/h, etc.

<u>This graph converts between miles and kilometres</u>

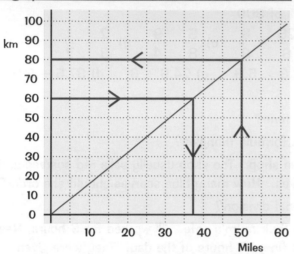

<u>This is how you can use it to answer questions:</u>

1) How many miles is 60 km?

ANS: Draw a line <u>straight across</u> from '60' on the 'km' axis 'til it <u>hits the line</u>, then go <u>straight down</u> to the 'miles' axis and read off the answer: <u>37.5 miles</u>

2) How many km is 50 miles?

ANS: Draw a line <u>straight up</u> from '50' on the 'miles' axis 'til it <u>hits the line</u>, then go <u>straight across</u> to the 'km' axis and read off the answer: <u>80 km</u>

GENERAL METHOD:

1) <u>Draw a line</u> from the <u>value</u> on one axis.
2) Keep going 'til you <u>hit the LINE</u>.
3) Then <u>change direction</u> and go straight to <u>the other axis</u>.
4) <u>Read off the new value</u> from the axis. <u>That's the answer</u>.

If you remember those 4 simple steps you can't go wrong — let's face it, Conversion Graphs are a doddle.

What the Gradient of a Graph Means

No matter what the graph, <u>THE MEANING OF THE GRADIENT</u> is always simply:

(y-axis UNITS)   PER   (x-axis UNITS)

<u>EXAMPLES:</u>

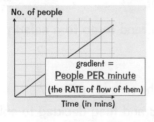

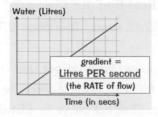

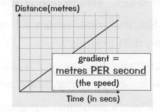

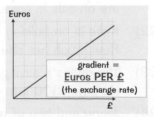

Some gradients have special names like <u>Exchange Rate</u> or <u>Speed</u>, but once you've written down '<u>something PER something</u>' using the y-axis and x-axis <u>UNITS</u>, it's pretty easy to work out what the gradient represents.

Right graph — we're not leaving here 'til I get some answers...

<u>Learn how to use a conversion graph</u> and <u>the meaning of gradients</u>.
Use the graph above to convert: 1) 15 miles to km,   2) 40 km to miles.

D/T and S/T Graphs

Ah, what could be better than a nice D/T graph? OK, so maybe there are some things that might be better — but you need to know about D/T graphs — and S/T graphs for that matter too — so best learn them now...

1) Distance-Time Graphs

Just remember these 3 important points:

> 1) At any point, <u>GRADIENT = SPEED</u>, but watch out for the UNITS.
> 2) The <u>STEEPER</u> the graph, the <u>FASTER</u> it's going.
> 3) <u>FLAT SECTIONS</u> are where it is <u>STOPPED</u>.

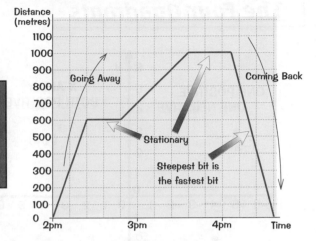

EXAMPLE: "What is the speed of the return section on the graph shown?"

<u>ANSWER:</u> Speed = gradient = 1000 m ÷ 30 mins = **33.33** <u>m/min</u>.

But m/min are naff units, so it's better to do it like this: 1 km ÷ 0.5 hrs = <u>2 km/h</u>

2) Speed-Time Graphs

A speed-time graph can <u>look</u> just the same as a distance-time graph but it means something <u>completely different</u>. The graph shown here is exactly the same shape as the one above, but the actual movements that they're describing are completely different.

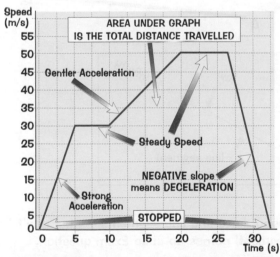

Remember these important points:

> 1) At any point, <u>GRADIENT = ACCELERATION</u>, (The UNITS are m/s² don't forget).
> 2) <u>NEGATIVE SLOPE</u> is <u>DECELERATION</u>.
> 3) <u>FLAT SECTIONS</u> are <u>STEADY SPEED</u>.
>
> [Higher level only:]
> 4) AREA UNDER GRAPH = DISTANCE TRAVELLED.

The D/T graph shows something <u>moving away</u> and then <u>back again</u> with <u>steady speeds</u> and <u>long stops</u>, rather like an ocean liner. The <u>S/T graph</u> on the other hand shows something that sets off from <u>rest</u>, <u>accelerates strongly</u>, <u>holds its speed</u>, then <u>accelerates</u> again up to a <u>maximum speed</u> which it holds for a while and then comes to a <u>dramatic halt</u> at the end. More like a <u>Ferrari</u> than an ocean liner...

Moan, moan, moan is all my slope ever does — he's just so negative...

It might not be the most exciting stuff, but you might just be asked about it the Exam. So learn the <u>7 important points</u> and the <u>two diagrams</u> then turn over and <u>write them all down</u>. Then kick back with these...

1) For the D/T graph shown above, work out the speed of the middle section in km/h.
2) For the S/T graph, work out the three different accelerations and the two steady speeds.

Coordinates, Lines and Line Segments

What could be more fun than points in one quadrant? <u>Lines</u> and <u>line segments</u>, that's what...

The Four Quadrants

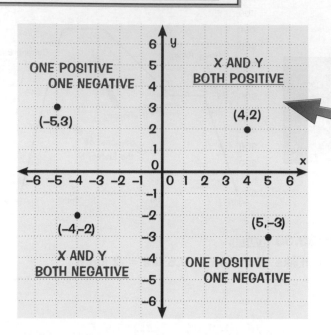

ONE POSITIVE
ONE NEGATIVE

(−5,3)

X AND Y
BOTH POSITIVE

(4,2)

(−4,−2)

(5,−3)

X AND Y
BOTH NEGATIVE

ONE POSITIVE
ONE NEGATIVE

A graph has <u>four different quadrants</u> (regions) where the x- and y- coordinates are either <u>positive</u> or <u>negative</u>.

This is the easiest region to deal with because here <u>all the coordinates are positive</u>.

You have to be more careful in the <u>other regions</u> though, because the x- and y- coordinates could be <u>negative</u>, and that always makes life more difficult.

Coordinates are always written in brackets like this: **(x, y)** — remember x is <u>across</u>, and y is <u>up</u>.

Lines and Line Segments...

1) You might be asked to find the length of a line AB: To be really precise, the line AB isn't actually a line — it's a <u>line segment</u>. Confused, read on...

2) A <u>line</u> is <u>straight</u> and continues <u>to infinity</u> (it goes on forever) in both directions.

3) A <u>line segment</u> is just <u>part</u> of a line — it has 2 end points.

4) So the length AB is just a <u>chunk</u> of the line running through A and B.

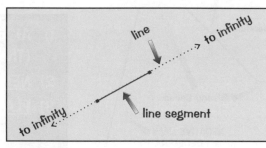

line

to infinity

to infinity

line segment

Welcome to Infinity
Population: ∞

<u>Don't worry too much</u> about lines and line segments — just don't panic if the term 'line segment' comes up in an Exam question.

Infinity can never actually be reached, which is just as well because it's a very weird place...

Don't go near angry parts of lines — they're segmental...

So that wasn't too taxing — you just need to know where on a graph coordinates are positive (and where they're negative). And that the first number is across and the second is up/down. Have a go at these questions to check that you've got both of those things nailed:

1) Write down the coordinates of the letters A to H on this graph:

2) What's the difference between a line and a line segment?

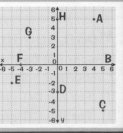

Midpoints and Lengths of Line Segments

Pythagoras is a bit of a hero really, how did people ever find the distance between two points without him? Well, probably with some sort of measuring stick — but who needs that when you can wield the power of the mighty right-angled triangle...

Finding the Midpoint of a Line Segment

This regularly comes up in Exams and is dead easy...

1) Find the average of the two x-coordinates, then do the same for the y-coordinates.
2) These will be the coordinates of the midpoint.

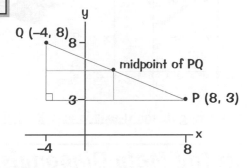

Example:

"Point P has coordinates (8, 3) and point Q has coordinates (-4, 8). Find the midpoint of the line PQ."

Solution:

Average of x-coordinates = (8 + -4)/2 = 2
Average of y-coordinates = (8 + 3)/2 = 5.5

So, coordinates of midpoint = (2, 5.5)

Use Pythagoras to find the Distance Between Points

You need to know how to find the straight-line distance between two points — the trick is to remember Pythagoras...

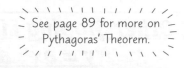
See page 89 for more on Pythagoras' Theorem.

EXAMPLE: "Point P has coordinates (8, 3) and point Q has coordinates (-4, 8). Find the length of PQ."

If you get a question like this, follow these rules and it'll all become breathtakingly simple:

1) Draw a sketch to show the right-angled triangle.
2) Find the lengths of the sides of the triangle.
3) Use Pythagoras to find the length of the diagonal. (That's your answer.)

SOLUTION:

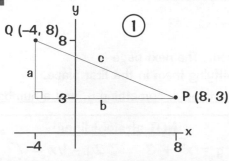

(2) Length of side a = 8 – 3 = 5
Length of side b = 8 – -4 = 12

(3) Use Pythagoras to find side c:
$c^2 = a^2 + b^2 = 5^2 + 12^2 = 25 + 144 = 169$
So: $c = \sqrt{169} = 13$

To find the midpoint — average, average, plonk...

After reading this page, you'll no doubt be as happy as Larry — the mystery of how to calculate the distance between two points without a ruler is solved. I think we'll all sleep a little easier at night. But before you do....

1) On the graph at the bottom of the previous page, find the coordinates of the points exactly midway between:
a) A and B   b) F and H   c) E and C
2) Point A has coordinates (10, 15) and point B has coordinates (6, 12). Find the length of the line AB.

Straight Line Graphs

If you thought I-spy was a fun game, wait 'til you play 'recognise the straight line graph from the equation'.

1) Vertical and Horizontal lines: 'x = a' and 'y = a'

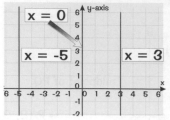

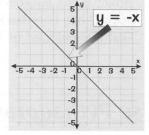
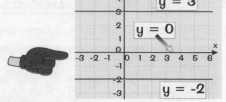

x = a is a <u>vertical line</u> through 'a' on the x-axis

y = a is a <u>horizontal line</u> through 'a' on the y-axis

Don't forget: <u>the y-axis is also the line x=0</u>

Don't forget: <u>the x-axis is also the line y=0</u>

2) The Main Diagonals: 'y = x' and 'y = –x'

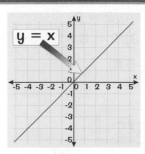

'y = x' is the <u>main diagonal</u> that goes <u>UPHILL</u> from left to right.

'y = -x' is the <u>main diagonal</u> that goes <u>DOWNHILL</u> from left to right.

3) Other Sloping Lines Through the origin: 'y = ax' and 'y = –ax'

y = ax and y = -ax are the equations for **A SLOPING LINE THROUGH THE ORIGIN**.

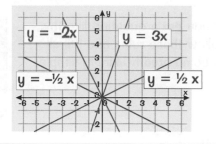

The value of '<u>a</u>' (known as the <u>gradient</u>) tells you the steepness of the line. The bigger 'a' is, the steeper the slope. A <u>MINUS SIGN</u> tells you it slopes <u>DOWNHILL</u>.

All Other Straight Lines

Other straight line equations are a little more complicated. The next page shows you how to draw them, but the first step is identifying them in the first place.

Remember: All straight line equations just contain '<u>something x, something y, and a number</u>'.

Straight lines:		NOT straight lines:	
x – y = 0	y = 2 + 3x	y = x³ + 3	2y – 1/x = 7
2y – 4x = 7	4x – 3 = 5y	1/y + 1/x = 2	x(3 – 2y) = 3
3y + 3x = 12	6y – x – 7 = 0	x² = 4 – y	xy + 3 = 0

My favourite line's y = 3x — it gets the ladies every time...

OK, so I can't offer a guarantee with that. But it's still worth learning all the graphs on this page and how to identify straight line equations. Once you think you know it, turn over the page and try and write it all down.

Plotting Straight Line Graphs

Sadly, this isn't about a sinister gang of straight line graphs, plotting to take over the world. But then that isn't likely to come up in the exam, and <u>drawing straight line graphs</u> is. There are <u>two</u> methods you can use:

1) The 'Table of 3 Values' Method

You can <u>easily</u> draw the graph of <u>any equation</u> using this <u>easy</u> method:

> 1) Choose <u>3 values of x</u> and <u>draw up a wee table</u>,
> 2) <u>Work out the y-values</u>,
> 3) <u>Plot the coordinates</u>, and <u>draw the line</u>.

If it's a <u>straight line equation</u>, the 3 points will be in a <u>dead straight line</u> with each other, which is the usual check you do when you've drawn it — <u>if they aren't</u>, then it could be a <u>curve</u> and you'll need to add <u>more values to your table</u> to find out what on earth's going on.

EXAMPLE: "Draw the graph of $y = 2x - 3$"

1) <u>Draw up a table</u> with some suitable values of x. Choosing $x = 0, 2, 4$ is usually OK. i.e.

X	0	2	4
Y			

2) <u>Find the y-values</u> by putting each x-value into the equation:

X	0	2	4
Y	−3	1	5

(e.g. When <u>x = 4</u>, $y = 2x - 3 = 2 \times 4 - 3 = \underline{5}$)

3) <u>Plot the points</u> and <u>draw the line</u>.

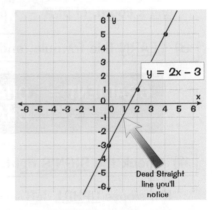

Dead Straight line you'll notice

2) The 'x = 0', 'y = 0' Method

> 1) <u>Set x=0</u> in the equation, and <u>find y</u> — this is where it <u>crosses the y-axis</u>.
> 2) <u>Set y=0</u> in the equation and <u>find x</u> — this is where it <u>crosses the x-axis</u>.
> 3) <u>Plot these two points</u> and <u>join them up with a straight line</u> — and just hope it should be a straight line, since with only 2 points you can't really tell, can you!

EXAMPLE: "Draw the graph of $5x + 3y = 15$"

Putting <u>x = 0</u> gives "$3y = 15$" $\Rightarrow$ <u>y = 5</u>
Putting <u>y = 0</u> gives "$5x = 15$" $\Rightarrow$ <u>x = 3</u>

So plot <u>(0, 5)</u> and <u>(3, 0)</u> on the graph and join them up with a straight line.

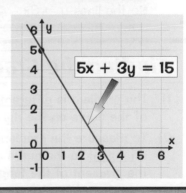

Only doing 2 points is risky unless you're sure the equation is definitely a straight line — but then that's the big thrill of living life on the edge, isn't it.

...x set himself to zero. "No!" cried y "I will not let you cross me again"...

I hope you enjoyed that extract from my new book — Methods of a Plotter. It's a psychological thriller about two letters who are bitter enemies. It's almost finished — it just needs a spell check. Now <u>learn</u> the details of these <u>two easy methods</u>, turn over and <u>write down all you know</u>. Then draw these graphs using <u>both</u> methods:

a) $y = 4 + x$ b) $4y + 3x = 12$ c) $y = 6 - 2x$

Finding the Gradient

Time to hit the slopes. Well, find them anyway...

Finding the Gradient

1) Find <u>TWO ACCURATE POINTS</u> and <u>COMPLETE THE TRIANGLE</u>

Both points should be in the <u>upper right quadrant</u> if possible (to keep all the numbers positive).

2) Find the <u>CHANGE IN Y</u> and the <u>CHANGE IN X</u>

Make sure you subtract the x coords. the <u>same way round</u> as you do the y coords.
E.g. y coord. of pt A – y coord. of pt B
<u>and</u> x coord. of pt A – x coord. of pt B

3) <u>LEARN</u> this formula, and use it:

$$\text{GRADIENT} = \frac{\text{CHANGE IN Y}}{\text{CHANGE IN X}}$$

4) Check the <u>SIGN'S</u> right.

If it slopes <u>UPHILL</u> left → right (⟋) <u>then it's positive</u>
If it slopes <u>DOWNHILL</u> left → right (⟍) <u>then it's negative</u>

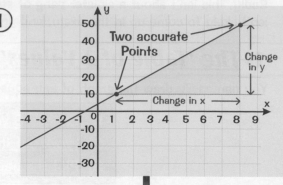

①
Two accurate Points
Change in y
Change in x

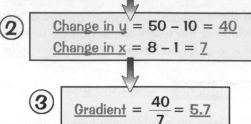

②
Change in y = 50 – 10 = <u>40</u>
Change in x = 8 – 1 = <u>7</u>

③
Gradient = $\frac{40}{7}$ = <u>5.7</u>

④
As the graph goes <u>UPHILL</u>, the gradient is positive.
So <u>5.7 is correct</u>, not -5.7

If you subtracted the coordinates the right way round, the sign should be correct. If it's not, go back and check what you've done.

Parallel and Perpendicular Lines

1) The equation of a straight line is <u>y = mx + c</u> (see p41) where <u>m</u> is the <u>gradient</u> and c is the y-intercept.

2) <u>Parallel</u> lines have the <u>same value of m</u>, i.e. the <u>same gradient</u>.
So the lines: y = 2x + 3, y = 2x and y = 2x – 4 are all <u>parallel</u>.

Ext. 3) If one line has <u>gradient m</u>, then any line <u>perpendicular</u> to it has <u>gradient</u> $\frac{-1}{m}$.
So the lines y = 3x – 4 and $y = \frac{-1}{3}x + 7$ are <u>perpendicular</u> to one another. Ext.

Finding the Gradient of a Curve is Trickier

1) The gradient is <u>different</u> at each point on a curve. E.g. the gradient of the curve on the right increases as you move along it from 0.

2) To measure the gradient at a particular point, draw a <u>tangent</u> to the curve at that point. Then calculate the gradient of the tangent using the method above.

A tangent is a line that just touches a curve, but doesn't cross it.

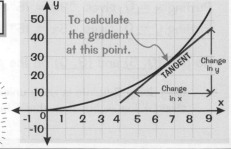

To calculate the gradient at this point.
TANGENT
Change in y
Change in x

Extended

Finding gradients is often an uphill battle...

Learn the <u>four steps</u> for finding a gradient then <u>turn over</u> and <u>write them down</u> from memory. Fun times ahoy.

1) Plot these 3 points on a graph: (0,3) (2,0) (5,-4.5) and then join them up with a straight line.
Now carefully apply the <u>four steps</u> to find the gradient of the line.

$y = mx + c$

Using '$y = mx + c$' is perhaps the 'proper' way of dealing with straight line equations, and it's a nice trick if you can do it.   The first thing you have to do though is <u>rearrange</u> the equation into the standard format like this:

<u>Straight line:</u>		<u>Rearranged into '$y = mx + c$'</u>	
$y = 2 + 3x$	$\rightarrow$	$y = 3x + 2$	(m=3, c=2)
$2y - 4x = 7$	$\rightarrow$	$y = 2x + 3\frac{1}{2}$	(m=2, c=3½)
$x - y = 0$	$\rightarrow$	$y = x + 0$	(m=1, c=0)
$4x - 3 = 5y$	$\rightarrow$	$y = 0.8x - 0.6$	(m=0.8, c=-0.6)
$3y + 3x = 12$	$\rightarrow$	$y = -x + 4$	(m=-1, c=4)

<u>REMEMBER</u>:   '<u>m</u>' equals the <u>gradient</u> of the line.
'<u>c</u>' is the '<u>y-intercept</u>' (where the graph hits the y-axis).

<u>BUT WATCH OUT</u>: people mix up 'm' and 'c' when they get something like $y = 5 + 2x$.
Remember, 'm' is the number <u>in front of the 'x'</u> and 'c' is the number <u>on its own</u>.

1) Sketching a Straight Line using $y = mx + c$

1) Get the equation into the form '<u>$y = mx + c$</u>'.

2) <u>Put a dot on the y-axis</u> at the value of c.

3) Then go <u>along one unit</u> and <u>up or down by the value of m</u> and make another dot.

4) <u>Repeat</u> the same 'step' in <u>both directions</u>.

5) Finally check that the gradient <u>looks right</u>.

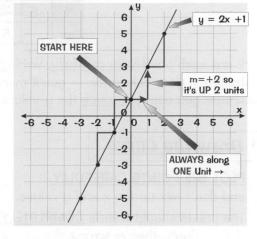

The graph shows the process for the equation '$y = 2x + 1$':
1) 'c' = 1, so put a first dot at y = 1 on the y-axis.
2) Go along 1 unit → and then up by 2 because 'm' = +2.
3) Repeat the same step, 1→ 2↑ in both directions.
4) CHECK: a gradient of <u>+2</u> should be <u>quite steep</u> and <u>uphill</u> left to right which it is, so it looks OK.

2) Finding the Equation Of a Straight Line Graph

This is the reverse process and is <u>EASIER</u>.

1) From the axes, <u>identify the two variables</u> (e.g. 'x and y' or 'h and t').

2) <u>Find the values</u> of '<u>m</u>' (gradient) and '<u>c</u>' (y-intercept) from the graph.

3) Using these values from the graph, <u>write down the equation</u> with the standard format '$y = mx + c$'.

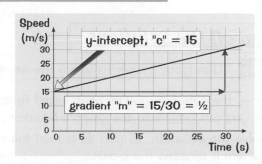

For the example above: '$S = \frac{1}{2}t + 15$'

Remember $y = mx + c$ — it'll keep you on the straight and narrow...

That, and remembering the <u>8 rules</u> for <u>drawing the lines</u> and <u>finding the equations</u>. And eating your greens.
1) Now, sketch these graphs: a) $y = 2 + x$ b) $y = x + 6$ c) $4x - 2y = 0$ d) $y = 1 - \frac{1}{2}x$
e) $x = 2y + 4$ f) $2x - 6y - 8 = 0$ g) $0.4x - 0.2y = 0.5$ h) $y = 3 - x + 2$

Quadratic Graphs

Quadratic functions can sound pretty darn impressive — "What did you do in maths today, dear?", "Drawing quadratic functions and solving them graphically, mum." Have no fear, with a bit of practice you too can sound this... er... cool, as well as picking up lots of marks in your exams.

Plotting and Solving Quadratic Functions

Quadratic functions are of the form $y = \underline{\text{anything with } x^2}$ (but not higher powers of x).
Notice that all these x^2 graphs have the same <u>SYMMETRICAL</u> bucket shape.

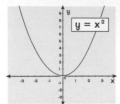
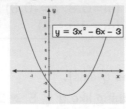
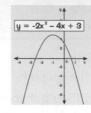

So when you plot a quadratic, remember that you're aiming for a symmetrical bucket shape — anything else is a sure sign that you've gone wrong. Here's how to tackle questions on quadratics.

1) Fill in The Table of Values

Example "Fill in the table of values for the equation $y = x^2 + 2x - 3$ and draw the graph."

x	-5	-4	-3	-2	-1	0	1	2	3
y		5		-3	-4	-3	0		

Work out each point <u>very carefully</u>, writing down all your working. Don't just plug it all straight in your calculator — you'll make mistakes. To check you're <u>doing it right</u>, make sure you can <u>reproduce</u> the y-values they've already given you.

2) Draw the Curve

1) <u>PLOT THE POINTS CAREFULLY</u>, and don't mix up the x and y values.

2) The points should form a <u>COMPLETELY SMOOTH CURVE</u>. If they don't, they're <u>wrong</u>.

<u>NEVER EVER</u> let one point drag your line off in some ridiculous direction. When a graph is generated from an equation, you never get spikes or lumps — only <u>MISTAKES</u>.

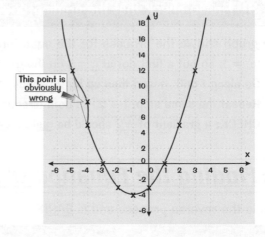

This point is <u>obviously wrong</u>

3) Read off the Solutions

Example "Use your graph to solve the equation $x^2 + 2x - 3 = 0$."

1) Look — the equation you've been asked to solve is what you get when you put <u>y=0</u> into the graph's equation, $y = x^2 + 2x - 3$.

2) To solve the equation, all you do is read the x-values where y = 0, i.e. where it crosses the x-axis.

3) So the solutions are <u>x = -3</u> and <u>x = 1</u>. (Quadratic eqns usually have 2 solutions.)

4) Celebrate the only way graphs know how: line dancing.

How refreshing — a page on graphs. Not seen one of those in a while...

You know the deal by now — learn what's on this page, then treat yourself to answering the question below.

1) Plot the graph of $y = x^2 - x - 6$ (use x-values from -4 to 5).
Use your graph to solve the equation $x^2 - x - 6 = 0$.

Some Harder Graphs to Learn

Graphs come in all sorts of shapes, sizes and wiggles — here are four more types of graph you need to know:

1) 1/x GRAPHS: $y = \frac{A}{x}$, or $xy = A$ (A is any number — positive or negative)

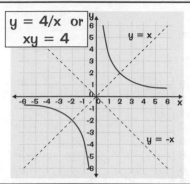

y = 4/x or xy = 4

These are all the same basic shape, except the negative ones are in opposite quadrants to the positive ones (as shown). The two halves of the graph don't touch.

They're all symmetrical about the lines $y = x$ and $y = -x$.

(You get this type of graph with inverse proportion — see P.54)

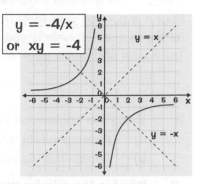

y = -4/x or xy = -4

2) x³ GRAPHS: $y = ax^3 + bx^2 + cx + d$ (b, c and/or d can be zero)

All x³ graphs have the same wiggle in the middle — sometimes it's a flat wiggle, sometimes it's more pronounced.

−x³ graphs always go down from top left, +x³ ones go up from bottom left.

(Note that x³ must be the highest power and there must be no other bits like 1/x etc.)

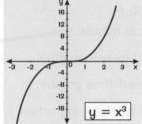

$y = x^3$

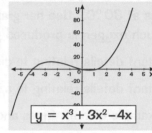

$y = x^3 + 3x^2 - 4x$

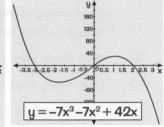

$y = -7x^3 - 7x^2 + 42x$

Like with quadratics (see previous page), you can use graphs like the ones on this page to find solutions of equations. E.g. from the third graph above you can see that the solutions of $-7x^3 - 7x^2 + 42x = 0$ are $x = -3$, $x = 0$ and $x = 2$.

3) 1/x² GRAPHS: $y = \frac{A}{x^2}$, or $x^2y = A$ (A is any number — positive or negative)

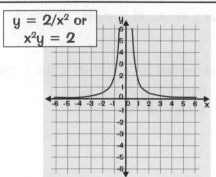

y = 2/x² or x²y = 2

These are a bit like the y=A/x graphs — except the two bits are next to each other.

The positive ones are above the x-axis and the negative ones are below the x-axis.

They're all symmetrical about the y-axis.

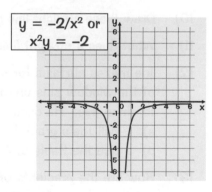

y = −2/x² or x²y = −2

4) kˣ GRAPHS: $y = k^x$ (k is some positive number)

1) These graphs curve upwards when k > 1.
2) They're always above the x-axis.
3) They all go through the point (0, 1).
4) For bigger values of k, the graph tails off towards zero more quickly on the left and climbs more steeply on the right.

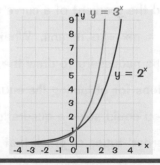

You might be asked to make a table of values and plot the graph for any of these types of equation — see the previous page.

Phew — that page could seriously drive you round the kˣ

Learn the graphs, both their equations and their shapes, then turn over and sketch 3 examples of each.

1) Describe the following graphs in words: a) $y = 3x^2 + 2$ b) $y = 4 - x^3$ c) $xy = 2$
   d) $x^2 + y^2 = 36$ e) $x = -7/y$ f) $3x^2 = y - 4x^3 + 2$ g) $y = x - x^2$ h) $y = 5^x$

Revision Summary

Aren't graphs great. I think everyone likes graphs.

Anyway, here are the scary questions to find out what you know. By the way, I hope you haven't started trying to kid yourself that these aren't proper maths questions so you don't have to bother with them. Oh no.

Maths is <u>packed</u> with <u>facts</u> — and you need to know them <u>to be able to do it</u>.
All these questions do is see how many of the simple facts you've learnt so far.
Try it now and scare yourself. Then learn some stuff and try again.

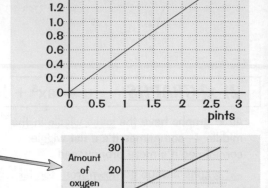

1) Using the conversion graph on the right:
   a) Approximately how many litres is 1.75 pints?
   b) Approximately how many pints is 1.6 litres?

2) What is the rule for deciding what the gradient of a graph represents?

3) Sarah has carried out an experiment to find the rate of photosynthesis at 30 °C. Use her graph to calculate how much oxygen is produced per minute.

4) Give three important details relating to distance-time graphs.

5) Give three important details relating to speed-time graphs.

6) Draw a typical example of both types and label the important features.

7) What does the area under a speed-time graph tell you?

8) What have Ferraris and ocean liners got to do with it?

9) Describe how to find the length of a line, and the midpoint, given the coordinates of the endpoints.

10) Draw these straight line graphs: a) x = 4, b) y = 0, c) y = x, d) y = -x, e) y = 3x, f) y = -3x

11) What does a straight line equation look like?

12) Joe makes curtains for a living. He knows that the length of material needed for a curtain is the length of the window plus one tenth of the length again. He works out the equation $y = x + \frac{1}{10}x$, to show this. He decides to draw a graph so staff can just read the values off that.
    a) Will Joe's graph be a straight line or a curve?
    b) Use the 'table of 3 values' method to draw Joe's graph.

13) How are the gradients of parallel lines related?

14) How do you find the gradient of a curve at a particular point?

15) Explain what 'y = mx + c' means. What do 'm' and 'c' represent?

16) List the five steps necessary to draw the graph of '5x = 2 + y' using 'y = mx + c'.

17) List the three steps for obtaining the equation from a straight line graph.

18) Describe how you could solve a quadratic equation using a graph.

19) List the four 'harder' types of graph that you should recognise.

20) Describe <u>in words</u> and with a sketch the forms of these graphs:
    $xy = a$; $y = mx + c$; $y = ax^2 + bx + c$; $y = ax^3 + bx^2 + cx + d$

Powers and Roots

Powers are a very useful shorthand: $2 \times 2 \times 2 \times 2 \times 2 \times 2 \times 2 = 2^7$ ('two to the power 7')

That bit is easy to remember. Unfortunately, there are <u>ten special rules</u> for powers that are not tremendously exciting, but you do need to know them for the Exam:

The Seven Easy Rules:

The first two only work for powers of the same number.

1) When <u>MULTIPLYING</u>, you <u>ADD THE POWERS</u>.   e.g. $3^4 \times 3^6 = 3^{6+4} = 3^{10}$

2) When <u>DIVIDING</u>, you <u>SUBTRACT THE POWERS</u>.   e.g. $5^4 \div 5^2 = 5^{4-2} = 5^2$

3) When <u>RAISING</u> one power to another, you <u>MULTIPLY THEM</u>.   e.g. $(3^2)^4 = 3^{2\times4} = 3^8$

4) $X^1 = X$, <u>ANYTHING</u> to the <u>POWER 1</u> is just <u>ITSELF</u>.   e.g. $3^1 = 3$, $6 \times 6^3 = 6^4$

5) $X^0 = 1$, <u>ANYTHING</u> to the <u>POWER 0</u> is just <u>ONE</u>.   e.g. $5^0 = 1$ $67^0 = 1$

6) $1^x = 1$, <u>1 TO ANY POWER</u> is <u>STILL JUST 1</u>.   e.g. $1^{23} = 1$ $1^{89} = 1$ $1^2 = 1$

7) <u>FRACTIONS</u> — Apply power to <u>both TOP and BOTTOM</u>.   e.g. $\left(1\frac{3}{5}\right)^3 = \left(\frac{8}{5}\right)^3 = \frac{8^3}{5^3} = \frac{512}{125}$

The Three Tricky Rules:

8) <u>NEGATIVE Powers — Turn it Upside-Down</u>

People do have quite a bit of difficulty remembering this.

Whenever you see a negative power you're supposed to immediately think:
"Aha, that means turn it the other way up and make the power positive".

Like this: e.g. $7^{-2} = \frac{1}{7^2} = \frac{1}{49}$ $\left(\frac{3}{5}\right)^{-2} = \left(\frac{5}{3}\right)^{+2} = \frac{5^2}{3^2} = \frac{25}{9}$

9) <u>FRACTIONAL POWERS</u>

> The power $\frac{1}{2}$ means <u>Square Root</u>,
> The power $\frac{1}{3}$ means <u>Cube Root</u>,
> The power $\frac{1}{4}$ means <u>Fourth Root</u> etc.

e.g. $25^{1/2} = \sqrt{25} = 5$
$64^{1/3} = \sqrt[3]{64} = 4$
$81^{1/4} = \sqrt[4]{81} = 3$ etc.

The one to really watch is when you get a <u>negative fraction</u> like $49^{-1/2}$ — people get mixed up and think that the minus is the square root, and forget to turn it upside down as well.

10) <u>TWO-STAGE FRACTIONAL POWERS</u>

They really like putting these in Exam questions so learn the method:
With fractional powers like $64^{5/6}$ always <u>split the fraction</u> into a <u>root</u> and a <u>power</u>,
and do them in that order: <u>root</u> first, then <u>power</u>: $(64)^{1/6 \times 5} = (64^{1/6})^5 = (2)^5 = 32$

Some Roots can be Positive or Negative

The <u>square root</u> of a number can be <u>positive</u> or <u>negative</u> (see p5).
The same is true for any <u>even root</u> of a number. <u>Odd roots</u> are only ever <u>positive</u>.

("<u>Even roots</u>" means square roots, fourth roots, sixth roots, etc. "<u>Odd roots</u>" means cube roots, fifth roots, seventh roots, etc.)

The root sign $\sqrt{y}$ only represents the positive root. So $\sqrt{4} = 2$ only.

> E.g.   If $x^4 = 625$, then $x = \pm\sqrt[4]{625} = \pm5$ If $x^5 = 1024$, then $x = \sqrt[5]{1024} = 4$

Extended

Square Roots? Must be a geomer-tree...*

Learn the <u>exciting rules</u> on this page. Then turn over and write them all down with <u>examples</u>. <u>Keep trying till you can</u>.

1) Simplify: a) $3^2 \times 3^6$ b) $4^3 / 4^2$ c) $(8^3)^4$ d) $(3^2 \times 3^3 \times 1^6)/3^5$ e) $7^3 \times 7 \times 7^2$

2) Evaluate   a) $(1/4)^{-3}$ b) 25^{-2} c) $25^{-1/2}$ d) $(27/216)^{-1/3}$ e) $625^{3/4}$ f) $125^{-2/3}$

3) Use your calculator to find: a) 5.2^{24} b) $40^{3/4}$ c) $\sqrt[5]{200}$

*winner of Best Maths Gag in a Supporting Role, International Algebra Awards 2010

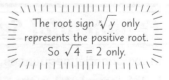

Finding the nth Term

"The nth term" is a formula with "n" in it which gives you <u>every term in a sequence</u> when you put different values for n in. How the formula looks depends on the type of sequence you're dealing with.

Common Difference Type: 'dn + (a – d)'

For any sequence such as 3, 7, 11, 15, where there is a <u>COMMON DIFFERENCE</u>:

you can always find 'the nth term' using the formula: **'nth term = dn + (a – d)'**

1) 'a' is simply the value of <u>THE FIRST TERM</u> in the sequence.
2) 'd' is simply the value of <u>THE COMMON DIFFERENCE</u> between the terms.
3) To get the <u>nth term</u>, you just find the values of '<u>a</u>' and '<u>d</u>' from the sequence and <u>stick them in the formula</u>. You don't replace n though — that wants to stay as n.
4) Of course <u>YOU HAVE TO LEARN THE FORMULA</u>, but life is like that.

Example: "Find the nth term of this sequence: 5, 8, 11, 14 ...."

1) The formula is dn + (a – d)
2) The <u>first term</u> is 5, so <u>a = 5</u>. The <u>common difference</u> is 3 so <u>d = 3</u>.
3) Putting these in the formula gives: 3n + (5 – 3) so the <u>nth term = 3n + 2</u>.

Changing Difference Type: 'a + (n – 1)d + ½(n – 1)(n – 2)C'

If the number sequence is one where the difference between the terms is <u>increasing or decreasing</u> then it gets a whole lot more complicated (as you can see from the above formula which you'll have to <u>learn</u>!). This time there are <u>THREE</u> letters to fill in:

'a' is the <u>FIRST TERM</u>,
'd' is the <u>FIRST DIFFERENCE</u> (between the first two numbers),
'C' is the <u>CHANGE BETWEEN ONE DIFFERENCE AND THE NEXT</u>.

Example: "Find the nth term of this sequence: 2, 5, 9, 14 ...."

1) The formula is   'a + (n – 1)d + ½(n – 1)(n – 2)C'
2) The <u>first term</u> is 2, so <u>a = 2</u>. The <u>first difference</u> is 3 so <u>d = 3</u>.
3) The <u>differences increase</u> by 1 each time so <u>C = +1</u>.

Putting these in the formula gives: '2 + (n – 1)3 + ½(n – 1)(n – 2) × 1'
Which becomes: $2 + 3n - 3 + ½n^2 - 1½n + 1$
Which simplifies to: $½n^2 + 1½n = ½n(n + 3)$ so the <u>nth term = ½n(n + 3)</u>.

Exponential Sequences: 'a × r^n'

In exponential sequences, you <u>multiply</u> by the <u>same number</u> each time to get from one term to the next. In the formula 'a' is the <u>FIRST TERM</u> and 'r' is the <u>NUMBER YOU MULTIPLY BY</u> to get to the next term.

Example: 3, 6, 12, 24, ...   The first term is 3 and you multiply by 2 each time,
so the <u>nth term = 3 × 2^n</u>.

If I've told you n times, I've told you (n + 1) times — learn this page...

Learn the <u>definition of the nth term</u>, and for each type learn the <u>steps for finding it</u> and <u>the formula</u>. Then try this question — it's a 3 minute game and you'll be locked in if your feet touch the floor more than 3 times.

1) Find the nth term of the following sequences:
a) 4, 7, 10, 13, ...   b) 3, 8, 13, 18, ...   c) 1, 3, 6, 10, 15, ...   d) 3, 4, 7, 12, ...

Basic Algebra

Normally I don't like to be too negative, but sometimes being negative is important...
Negative numbers crop up everywhere so you need to learn this rule for dealing with them:

+	+ makes	+
+	– makes	–
–	+ makes	–
–	– makes	+

Only to be used when:

1) Multiplying or dividing:

e.g. $-2 \times 3 = \underline{-6}$, $-8 \div -2 = \underline{+4}$ $-4p \times -2 = \underline{+8p}$

2) Two signs are together:

e.g. $5 - -4 = 5 + 4 = \underline{9}$ $4 + -6 - -7 = 4 - 6 + 7 = \underline{5}$

Letters Multiplied Together

Watch out for these combinations of letters in algebra that regularly catch people out:

1) abc means $a \times b \times c$. The ×'s are often left out to make it clearer.
2) gn^2 means $g \times n \times n$. Note that only the n is squared, not the g as well.
3) $(gn)^2$ means $g \times g \times n \times n$. The brackets mean that <u>BOTH</u> letters are squared.
4) $p(q - r)^3$ means $p \times (q - r) \times (q - r) \times (q - r)$. Only the brackets get cubed.
5) -3^2 is a bit ambiguous. It should either be written $(-3)^2 = 9$, or $-(3^2) = -9$

D.O.T.S. — The Difference Of Two Squares:

$$a^2 - b^2 = (a + b)(a - b)$$

The 'difference of two squares' (D.O.T.S. for short) is where you have 'one thing squared' take away 'another thing squared'. Too many people have more trouble than they should with this, probably because they don't make enough effort to learn it as a separate item in its own right. Best learn it now, eh, before it's too late.

1) Factorise $9P^2 - 16Q^2$. Answer: $9P^2 - 16Q^2 = (3P + 4Q)(3P - 4Q)$
2) Factorise $1 - T^4$. Answer: $1 - T^4 = (1 + T^2)(1 - T^2)$
3) Factorise $3K^2 - 75H^2$. Answer: $3K^2 - 75H^2 = 3(K^2 - 25H^2) = 3(K + 5H)(K - 5H)$

Ahhh algebra, it's as easy as abc, or 2(ab) + c, or something like that...

Learn everything on this page. Now <u>turn over and write it all down</u>. Then do these without a calculator:
1) a) -4×-3 b) $-4 + -5 + 3$ c) $(3x + -2x - 4x) \div (2 + -5)$ d) $120 \div -40$
2) If m=2 and n=-3 work out: a) mn^2 b) $(mn)^3$ c) $m(4+n)^2$ d) n^3 e) $3m^2n^3 + 2mn$
3) Factorise: a) $x^2 - 16y^2$ b) $49 - 81p^2q^2$ c) $12y^2x^6 - 48k^4m^8$

Basic Algebra

The next two pages have some really important algebra rules. You'll find yourself using these at least once a day for the rest of your lives*, so it's a good idea to learn them now rather than struggling later on...

1) Terms

Before you can do anything else, you must understand what a term is:

1) **A TERM IS A COLLECTION OF NUMBERS, LETTERS AND BRACKETS, ALL MULTIPLIED/DIVIDED TOGETHER.**

2) Terms are separated by <u>+ and – signs</u>. E.g. $4x^2 - 3py - 5 + 3p$

3) Terms always have a + or – attached to the <u>front of them</u>.
E.g.

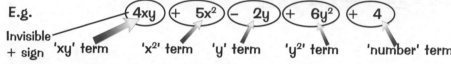

Invisible + sign   'xy' term   'x²' term   'y' term   'y²' term   'number' term

2) Simplifying or 'Collecting Like Terms'

<u>EXAMPLE</u>: Simplify $2x - 4 + 5x + 6$

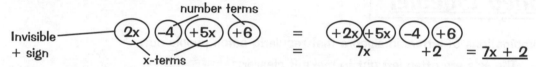

Invisible + sign   x-terms   number terms

$$= (+2x)(+5x)(-4)(+6)$$
$$= 7x \qquad +2 \quad = \underline{7x + 2}$$

1) Put <u>bubbles</u> round each term — be sure you capture the <u>+/– sign</u> in front of each.

2) Then you can move the bubbles into the <u>best order</u> so that <u>like terms</u> are together.

3) "Like terms" have exactly the same combination of letters, e.g. x-terms or xy-terms.

4) <u>Combine like terms</u> by adding or subtracting.

3) Multiplying out Brackets

1) The thing <u>outside</u> the brackets multiplies <u>each separate term</u> inside the brackets.

2) When letters are multiplied together, they are just written next to each other, pq.

3) Remember, $R \times R = R^2$, and TY^2 means $T \times Y \times Y$, whilst $(TY)^2$ means $T \times T \times Y \times Y$.

4) Remember a minus outside the bracket <u>REVERSES ALL THE SIGNS</u> when you multiply.

1) $3(2x + 5) = \underline{6x + 15}$ 2) $4p(3r - 2t) = \underline{12pr - 8pt}$

3) $-4(3p^2 - 7q^3) = -12p^2 + 28q^3$ (note both signs have been reversed — Rule 4)

5) <u>DOUBLE BRACKETS</u> — you get <u>4 terms</u>, and usually 2 of them combine to leave <u>3 terms</u>.

$$(2P - 4)(3P + 1) = (2P \times 3P) + (2P \times 1) + (-4 \times 3P) + (-4 \times 1)$$
$$= 6P^2 + 2P \qquad -12P \qquad -4$$
$$= \underline{6P^2 - 10P - 4} \qquad \text{(these 2 combine together)}$$

6) <u>SQUARED BRACKETS</u> — Always write these out as <u>TWO BRACKETS</u>:

E.g. $(3d + 5)^2$ should be written out as $(3d + 5)(3d + 5)$ and then worked out as above.
YOU SHOULD ALWAYS GET <u>FOUR</u> TERMS from a pair of brackets.
The usual <u>WRONG ANSWER</u> is $(3d + 5)^2 = 9d^2 + 25$ (eeek)
It should be: $(3d + 5)^2 = (3d + 5)(3d + 5) = 9d^2 + 15d + 15d + 25 = \underline{9d^2 + 30d + 25}$

Extended

Basic Algebra

4) Factorising — putting brackets in

This is the <u>exact reverse</u> of multiplying-out brackets. Here's the method to follow:

1) Take out the <u>biggest number</u> that goes into all the terms.

2) <u>Take each letter in turn</u> and take out the <u>highest power</u> (e.g. x, x^2 etc) that will go into EVERY term.

3) Open the brackets and fill in all the bits needed to <u>reproduce each term</u>.

<u>EXAMPLE:</u>   "Factorise $15x^4y + 20x^2y^3z - 35x^3yz^2$"

<u>ANSWER:</u> $5x^2y(3x^2 + 4y^2z - 7xz^2)$

Biggest number that'll divide into 15, 20 and 35.

Highest powers of x and y that will go into all three terms.

z was not in ALL terms so it can't come out as a <u>common factor</u>.

Some expressions need to be factorised in more than one set of brackets.

<u>EXAMPLE:</u> "Factorise $3x + xy - 6 - 2y$"

<u>ANSWER:</u> $3x + xy - 6 - 2y = x(3 + y) - 2(3 + y) = (x - 2)(3 + y)$

> <u>REMEMBER:</u> The bits <u>taken out</u> and put at the front are the <u>common factors</u>.
> The bits <u>inside the brackets</u> are what's needed to get back to the <u>original terms</u> if you multiply the brackets out again.

5) Algebraic Fractions

I love algebraic fractions.

The basic rules are exactly the same as for ordinary fractions.

1) Multiplying (easy)

Multiply top and bottom separately and cancel if possible:

$$\text{e.g.} \quad \frac{st}{10w^3} \times \frac{35s^2tw}{6} = \frac{35s^3t^2w}{60w^3} = \frac{7s^3t^2}{12w^2}$$

2) Dividing (easy)

Turn the second one upside down, then multiply and cancel if possible:

$$\text{e.g.} \quad \frac{12}{p+4} \div \frac{4(p-3)}{3(p+4)} = \frac{12}{p+4}^{3} \times \frac{3(p+4)}{4(p-3)} = \frac{9}{p-3}$$

3) Adding/subtracting (not so easy)

Always get a common denominator, i.e. same bottom line (by cross-multiplying) and then <u>ADD TOP LINES ONLY</u>:

$$\frac{t-2p}{3t-p} - \frac{1}{3} = \frac{3(t-2p)}{3(3t-p)} - \frac{1(3t-p)}{3(3t-p)} = \frac{3t-6p-3t+p}{3(3t-p)} = \frac{-5p}{3(3t-p)}$$

Go forth and multiply out brackets...

Learn the details on these two pages. Then get your nimble maths brains around these:

1) Simplify: $5x + 3y - 4 - 2y - x$

2) Expand $2pq(3p - 4q^2)$

3) Expand $(2g + 5)(4g - 2)$

4) Factorise $14x^2y^3 + 21xy^2 - 35x^3y^4$

5) Simplify $\frac{5abc^3}{18de} \div \frac{15abd^2}{9ce}$

6) Simplify $\frac{3}{5} + \frac{5g}{3g-4}$

Extended

Extended

Making Formulas from Words

These can seem a bit confusing but they're not as bad as they look, once you know the "tricks of the trade", as it were. There are two main types.

Type 1

In this type there are <u>instructions about what to do with a number</u> and you have to write it as a <u>formula</u>. The only things they're likely to want you to do in the formula are:

| 1) Multiply x | 2) Divide x | 3) Square x (x^2) | 4) Add or subtract a number |

Example 1: "To find y, multiply x by three and then subtract four"

Answer: Start with x $\rightarrow$ $3x$ $\rightarrow$ $3x - 4$ so $\underline{y = 3x - 4}$

                      Times it by 3   Subtract 4   (not too gruelling, is it?)

Example 2: This is probably the most difficult you'd ever get:
"To find y, square x, divide this by three and then subtract seven. Write a formula for y."

Answer: Start with x $\rightarrow$ x^2 $\rightarrow$ $\dfrac{x^2}{3}$ $\rightarrow$ $\dfrac{x^2}{3} - 7$ $y = \dfrac{x^2}{3} - 7$

               Square it   Divide it by 3   Subtract 7

The BODMAS rules apply in algebraic formulas like these — see p6.

Type 2

This is a bit harder. <u>You have to make up a formula</u> by putting in letters like 'C' for '<u>cost</u>' or 'n' for '<u>number of something-or-others</u>'. Although it may look confusing the formulas usually turn out to be <u>PRETTY SIMPLE</u>, so make sure you give it a go.

Example: Dean is designing a rectangular sign. The length of the sign must be 1.5 m greater than its width. The plastic the sign is to be made from costs £9 per m². Write a formula that Dean could use to work out the cost, C, of the plastic needed to make a sign of width w m.

Answer: The width of the sign is w m, so the length is (w + 1.5) m.

The area of the sign = $l \times w = (w + 1.5) \times w = w^2 + 1.5w$

So the cost of the plastic is $C = 9(w^2 + 1.5w)$

              or $C = 9w^2 + 13.5w$

I'm so impressed with this page that words fail me...

Nope. I got nothin'. Best just do these questions:

1) The value of y is found by taking x, multiplying it by five and then subtracting three. Write down a formula for y in terms of x.

2) Lauren has a part-time job as a waitress. She earns £6 per hour, plus tips. She saves half of the money she earns, and pays £5 per week in bus fares to get to work. If she works h hours per week, and receives a total £t in tips that week, write down a formula for the total amount, A, that Lauren has left to spend.

Solving Equations

Solving equations means finding the value of x from something like: $3x + 5 = 4 - 5x$.
Now, not a lot of people know this, but <u>exactly the same method applies</u> to both <u>solving equations</u> and <u>rearranging formulas</u>, as illustrated over the next two pages.

> 1) EXACTLY THE SAME METHOD APPLIES TO BOTH FORMULAS AND EQUATIONS.
> 2) THE SAME SEQUENCE OF STEPS APPLIES EVERY TIME.

To illustrate the sequence of steps we'll use this equation: $\sqrt{2 - \dfrac{x+4}{2x+5}} = 3$

The Six Steps Applied to Equations

1) Get rid of any square root signs by <u>squaring both sides</u>: $\quad 2 - \dfrac{x+4}{2x+5} = 9$

2) Get everything off the bottom by <u>cross-multiplying</u> up to <u>EVERY OTHER TERM</u>:

$$② - \dfrac{x+4}{2x+5} = ⑨ \quad \Rightarrow \quad 2(2x+5) - (x+4) = 9(2x+5)$$

3) <u>Multiply out</u> any brackets: $\quad 4x + 10 - x - 4 = 18x + 45$

4) Collect all <u>subject terms</u> on one side of the '=' and all <u>non-subject terms</u> on the other. Remember to reverse the +/− sign of any term that crosses the '='

$+18x$ moves across the '=' and becomes $-18x$ $\qquad 4x + 10 - x - 4 = 18x + 45$
$+10$ moves across the '=' and becomes -10
-4 moves across the '=' and becomes $+4$ $\qquad 4x - x - 18x = 45 - 10 + 4$

5) <u>Combine together like terms</u> on each side of the equation, and reduce it to the form '$\underline{Ax = B}$', where A and B are just numbers (or bunches of letters, in the case of formulas): $\qquad -15x = 39$
('Ax = B':
$A = -15$, $B = 39$, x is the subject)

6) Finally <u>slide the A underneath the B</u> to give '$x = \dfrac{B}{A}$', divide, and that's your answer. $\qquad x = \dfrac{39}{-15} = -2.6$
So $\underline{x = -2.6}$

The Seventh Step (if You Need It)

If the term you're trying to find is squared, don't panic.

Follow steps 1) to 6) like normal, but solve it for x^2 instead of x: $\qquad x^2 = 9$
$$x = \pm 3$$

7) <u>Take the square root</u> of both sides and stick a ± sign in front of the expression on the right:
Don't forget the ± sign...
(See p5 if you don't know what I mean).

Solving equations — more fun than greasing a seal...

Definitely. I never ever exaggerate. Learn the <u>7 steps</u> for <u>solving equations</u>. Then have a go at answering these:

1) Solve these equations: a) $5(x + 2) = 8 + 4(5 - x)$ b) $\dfrac{4}{x+3} = \dfrac{6}{4-x}$ c) $x^2 - 21 = 3(5 - x^2)$

Rearranging Formulas

Rearranging formulas means making one letter the subject, e.g. getting 'y= ' from '2x + z = 3(y + 2p).'
Generally speaking 'solving equations' is easier, but don't forget:

> 1) EXACTLY THE SAME METHOD APPLIES TO BOTH FORMULAS AND EQUATIONS
> 2) THE SAME SEQUENCE OF STEPS APPLIES EVERY TIME.

We'll illustrate this by making 'y' the subject of this formula: $M = \sqrt{2K - \dfrac{K^2}{2y + 1}}$

The Six Steps Applied to Formulas

1) Get rid of any square root signs by __squaring both sides__: $M^2 = 2K - \dfrac{K^2}{2y + 1}$

2) Get everything off the bottom by __cross-multiplying__ up to __EVERY OTHER TERM__:

$$M^2 = 2K - \frac{K^2}{2y + 1} \Rightarrow M^2(2y + 1) = 2K(2y + 1) - K^2$$

3) __Multiply out__ any brackets: $\qquad 2yM^2 + M^2 = 4Ky + 2K - K^2$

4) Collect all __subject terms__ on one side of the '=' and all __non-subject terms__ on the other. Remember to reverse the +/− sign of any term that crosses the '='.

+4Ky moves across the '=' and becomes −4Ky $\qquad 2yM^2 + M^2 = 4Ky + 2K - K^2$
+M² moves across the '=' and becomes −M² $\qquad 2yM^2 - 4Ky = -M^2 + 2K - K^2$

5) __Combine together like terms__ on each side of the equation, and reduce it to the form '__Ax = B__', where x is the subject and A and B are just bunches of numbers and letters which __DON'T include__ the subject. Note that the LHS has to be __FACTORISED__:

$$(2M^2 - 4K)y = 2K - K^2 - M^2$$

('Ax = B' i.e. $A = (2M^2 - 4K)$, $B = 2K - K^2 - M^2$, y is the subject)

6) Finally __slide the A underneath the B__ to give '$x = \dfrac{B}{A}$',
(cancel if possible) and that's your answer. $\qquad$ So $y = \dfrac{2K - K^2 - M^2}{(2M^2 - 4K)}$

The Seventh Step (if You Need It)

$$M = \sqrt{2K - \frac{K^2}{2y^2 + 1}}$$

If the term you're trying to make the subject of the equation is squared, this is what you do:

Follow steps 1) to 6), $\quad y^2 = \dfrac{2K - K^2 - M^2}{(2M^2 - 4K)} \quad$ (I've skipped steps 1) - 6) because they're exactly the
and then... $\qquad\qquad\qquad\qquad\qquad\qquad\quad$ same as the first example — but with y^2 instead of y.)

7) __Take the square root__ of both sides and stick a ± sign in front of the expression on the right: $\quad y = \pm\sqrt{\dfrac{2K - K^2 - M^2}{(2M^2 - 4K)}} \quad$ Remember — square roots can be +ve or −ve. See p5.

If I could rearrange my subjects, I'd have maths all day every day...

But that's probably just me. Learn the __7 steps__ for __rearranging formulas__. Then get rearrangin' with these:
1) Rearrange '$F = \frac{9}{5}C + 32$' from 'F= ', to 'C= ' and then back the other way.
2) Make p the subject of these: a) $\dfrac{p}{p + y} = 4$ b) $\dfrac{1}{p} = \dfrac{1}{q} + \dfrac{1}{r}$ c) $\dfrac{1}{p^2} = \dfrac{1}{q} + \dfrac{1}{r}$

Simultaneous Equations

Simultaneous equations are one of the all-time classic algebra topics. The rules for solving them are really quite simple, but <u>you must follow ALL the steps, in the right order, and treat them as a strict method</u>.

Six Steps For Simultaneous Equations

We'll use these two equations for our example: $2x = 6 - 4y$ and $-3 - 3y = 4x$

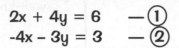

1) <u>Rearrange both equations</u> into the form <u>$ax + by = c$</u> where a, b, c are numbers, (which can be negative). Also label the two equations —①and —②

$$2x + 4y = 6 \quad —①$$
$$-4x - 3y = 3 \quad —②$$

2) You need to <u>match up the numbers in front</u> (the 'coefficients') of either the x's or y's in both equations. To do this you may need to multiply one or both equations by a suitable number. You should then relabel them: —③ and —④

$$①\times 2: \quad 4x + 8y = 12 \quad —③$$
$$-4x - 3y = 3 \quad —④$$

3) <u>Add or subtract the two equations</u> to eliminate the terms with the same coefficient
If the <u>coefficients are the same</u> (both +ve or both −ve) then **SUBTRACT**
If the <u>coefficients are opposite</u> (one +ve and one −ve) then **ADD**

$$③ + ④ \quad 0x + 5y = 15$$

4) Solve the resulting equation to find whichever letter is left in it.

$$5y = 15 \quad \Rightarrow \underline{y = 3}$$

5) Substitute this value back into equation ① and solve it to find the other quantity.

Sub in ①: $\quad 2x + 4\times 3 = 6 \quad \Rightarrow \quad 2x + 12 = 6 \quad \Rightarrow \quad 2x = -6 \quad \Rightarrow \underline{x = -3}$

6) Then substitute both these values into equation ② to make sure it works.
If it doesn't then you've done something wrong and you'll have to do it all again.

Sub x and y in ②: $\quad -4\times -3 - 3\times 3 = 12 - 9 = \underline{3}$, which is right, so it's worked.
So the solutions are: $\quad \underline{x = -3}, \quad \underline{y = 3}$

Sunday morning, lemon squeezy and simultaneous linear equations...

...all easy apparently. Easy or not, you need to learn the <u>6 steps</u> on this page. Remember, you only know them when you can write them all out from memory, so turn over the page and see if you can write down all six.
1) Apply the six steps to find F and G given that $2F - 10 = 4G$ and $3G = 4F - 15$

Direct and Inverse Proportion

You might remember direct and inverse proportion from such pages as page 21.
Now you need to know a little bit more about the algebra side of proportion questions.

Direct Proportion: y = kx

BOTH INCREASE TOGETHER

1) The graph of y against x is a <u>straight line</u> <u>through the origin</u>: <u>y = kx</u>

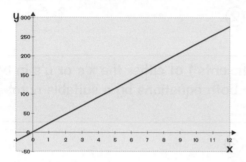

2) In a table of values the <u>MULTIPLIER</u> is the <u>same for x and y</u>, i.e. if you <u>double</u> one of them, you <u>double</u> the other, if you <u>times one of them by 3</u>, you <u>times the other by 3</u>, etc.

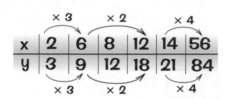

3) The <u>RATIO</u> $\frac{x}{y}$ is the same for <u>all pairs</u> of values, i.e from the table above:

$$\frac{2}{3} = \frac{6}{9} = \frac{8}{12} = \frac{12}{18} = \frac{14}{21} = \frac{56}{84} = 0.6667$$

Inverse Proportion: y = k/x

One <u>INCREASES</u> , one <u>DECREASES</u>

1) The graph of y against x is the well-known y = k/x graph:

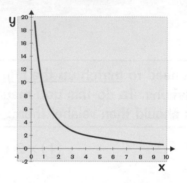

2) In a table of values the <u>MULTIPLIER</u> for one of them becomes a <u>DIVIDER</u> for the other, i.e. if you <u>double one</u>, you <u>half the other</u>, if you <u>treble one</u>, you <u>divide the other by three</u>, etc.

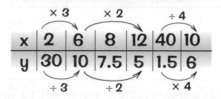

3) The <u>PRODUCT</u> xy (x times y) is the <u>same</u> for <u>all pairs of values</u>, i.e. in the table above:

$$2 \times 30 = 6 \times 10 = 8 \times 7.5 = 12 \times 5$$
$$= 40 \times 1.5 = 10 \times 6 = \underline{60}$$

Inverse Square Variation

You can have all sorts of relationships between x and y, like $y = kx^2$ or $y = k/x^3$ etc. as detailed on the next page. The most important type is <u>$y = k/x^2$</u> and is called '<u>INVERSE SQUARE</u>' variation. <u>DON'T MIX UP THIS NAME</u> with <u>inverse proportion</u>, which is just y = k/x.

<u>*A bear, ate a square, in underwear (that's a square in verse, actually...)*</u>

Learn the <u>3 key features</u> for both <u>direct</u> and <u>inverse</u> proportion. Then <u>turn over</u> and <u>write them all down</u>.
1) Give examples of 2 real quantities that exhibit: a) direct- and b) inverse proportion.
2) Make up your own tables of values which show: a) direct proportion   b) inverse proportion

Variation

This page shows you how to deal with questions which involve statements like these:
  'y is proportional to the square of x'   't is proportional to the square root of h'
  'D varies with the cube of t'   'V is inversely proportional to r cubed'
To deal successfully with things like this <u>you must remember this method</u>:

Method:

1) <u>Convert the sentence into a proportionality</u>,
  using the symbol '$\propto$' which means '<u>is proportional to</u>'.

2) <u>Replace '$\propto$' with '$=k$'</u> to make an <u>EQUATION</u>:

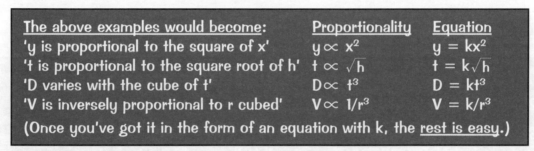

<u>The above examples would become:</u>	Proportionality	Equation
'y is proportional to the square of x'	$y \propto x^2$	$y = kx^2$
't is proportional to the square root of h'	$t \propto \sqrt{h}$	$t = k\sqrt{h}$
'D varies with the cube of t'	$D \propto t^3$	$D = kt^3$
'V is inversely proportional to r cubed'	$V \propto 1/r^3$	$V = k/r^3$

(Once you've got it in the form of an equation with k, the <u>rest is easy</u>.)

3) <u>Find a PAIR OF VALUES of x and y</u> somewhere in the question,
  and <u>SUBSTITUTE</u> them into the equation with the <u>sole purpose of finding k</u>.

4) <u>Put the value of k back into the equation</u>
  and it's now ready to use, e.g. $y = 3x^2$.

5) <u>INEVITABLY, they'll ask you to find y</u>,
  having given you a value for x (or vice versa).

Example:

The time taken for a duck to fall down a chimney (it happens!) is inversely proportional to the diameter of the flue. If she took 25 seconds to descend a chimney of diameter 0.3 m, how long would it take her to get down one of 0.2 m diameter?

(Notice there's no mention of 'writing an equation' or 'finding k'
— it's up to <u>YOU</u> to remember the method for yourself.)

<u>ANSWER</u>:

1) Write it as a <u>proportionality</u>, then an <u>equation</u>: $t \propto 1/d$ i.e. $t = k/d$
2) <u>Sub in the given values</u> for the two variables: $25 = k/0.3$
3) Rearrange the equation to <u>find k</u>: $k = 25 \times 0.3 = 7.5$
4) Put k <u>back in</u> the formula: $t = 7.5/d$
5) <u>Sub in new value</u> for d: $t = 7.5/0.2 = \underline{37.5 \text{ secs}}$

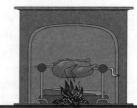

Joy $\propto$ 1/algebra...

This is all pretty straightforward. As long as you learn the <u>five steps of the method</u> plus the <u>four examples</u>. Then <u>turn over and write them all down</u>. Then do these questions. Then make me a lovely cup of tea. ☺

1) The frequency of a pendulum is inversely proportional to the square root of its length. If the pendulum swings with a frequency of 0.5 Hz when the length is 80 cm, what frequency will it have with a length of 50 cm, and what length will give a frequency of 0.7 Hz?

Factorising Quadratics

There are several ways of solving a quadratic equation as detailed on the following pages. You need to know all the methods.

Factorising a Quadratic

'Factorising a quadratic' means 'putting it into 2 brackets'.

(There are several different methods for doing this, so stick with the one you're happiest with. If you have no preference then learn the one below.)

The standard format for quadratic equations is: $ax^2 + bx + c = 0$
Most Exam questions have <u>a = 1</u>, making them <u>much easier</u>.

    E.g. $x^2 + 3x + 2 = 0$ (See next page for when a is not 1)

Factorising Method When a = 1

1) <u>ALWAYS</u> rearrange into the <u>STANDARD FORMAT</u>: $ax^2 + bx + c = 0$

2) Write down the <u>TWO BRACKETS</u> with the x's in: (x   )(x   )=0

3) Then <u>find 2 numbers</u> that <u>MULTIPLY to give 'c'</u> (the end number) but also <u>ADD/SUBTRACT to give 'b'</u> (the coefficient of x)

4) Put them in and check that the +/− signs work out properly.

An Example

"Solve $x^2 - x = 12$ by factorising."

ANSWER:

1) <u>First rearrange it</u> (into the standard format): $x^2 - x - 12 = 0$

2) a = 1, so the initial brackets are (as ever):   <u>(x   )(x   ) = 0</u>

3) We now want to look at <u>all pairs of numbers</u> that <u>multiply to give c</u> (=12), but which also <u>add or subtract to give the value of b</u>:

    1×12 Add/subtract to give: **13 or 11**
    2×6 Add/subtract to give: **8 or 4**
    3×4 Add/subtract to give: **7 or ①** ← this is what we're after (=±b)

4) So 3 and 4 will give b = ±1, so put them in: <u>(x   3)(x   4)=0</u>

5) <u>Now fill in the +/− signs</u> so that the 3 and 4 add/subtract to give -1 (=b), Clearly it must be +3 and −4 so we'll have: <u>(x + 3)(x − 4)=0</u>

6) <u>As an ESSENTIAL check, EXPAND the brackets</u> out again to make sure they give the original equation:
    $(x + 3)(x - 4) = x^2 + 3x - 4x - 12 = \underline{x^2 - x - 12}$

> We're not finished yet mind, because <u>(x + 3)(x − 4) = 0</u> is only the <u>factorised form of the equation</u> — we have yet to give the actual <u>SOLUTIONS</u>. This is very easy:

7) <u>THE SOLUTIONS</u> are simply <u>the two numbers in the brackets</u>, but with <u>OPPOSITE +/− SIGNS</u>: i.e. x = -3 or +4

> Make sure you remember that last step. <u>It's the difference</u> between <u>SOLVING THE EQUATION</u> and merely <u>factorising it</u>.

Extended
Extended
Extended

Factorising Quadratics

When 'a' is not 1   E.g. $3x^2 + 5x + 2 = 0$

The basic method is still the same but it's <u>a lot messier</u>. Chances are, the Exam question will be with a=1, so <u>make sure you can do that type easily</u>. Only then should you try to get to grips with these harder ones.

An Example   "Solve $3x^2 + 7x = 6$ by factorising."

1) <u>First rearrange it</u> (into the standard format): $\underline{3x^2 + 7x - 6 = 0}$

2) Now because a = 3, the two x-terms in the brackets will have to multiply to give $3x^2$
   so the initial brackets will have to be: <u>$(3x\quad)(x\quad)=0$</u>

   (i.e. <u>you put in the x-terms first</u>, with coeffts. that will multiply to give 'a')

3) We now want to look at <u>all pairs of numbers</u> that <u>multiply with each other to give 'c'</u>
   (=6, ignoring the minus sign for now):   i.e. 1×6 and 2×3

4) <u>Now the difficult bit</u>: to find the combination which does this:

<u>multiply with the 3x and x terms in the brackets and then
add or subtract to give the value of b (=7)</u>:

The best way to do this is by trying out all the possibilities in the brackets until you find the combination that works. Don't forget that <u>EACH PAIR</u> of numbers can be tried in <u>TWO</u> different positions:

$(3x\quad 1)(x\quad 6)$ <u>multiplies</u> to give <u>18x and 1x</u> which <u>add/subtract</u> to give <u>19x or 17x</u>

$(3x\quad 6)(x\quad 1)$ <u>multiplies</u> to give <u>3x and 6x</u> which <u>add/subtract</u> to give <u>9x or 3x</u>

$(3x\quad 3)(x\quad 2)$ <u>multiplies</u> to give <u>6x and 3x</u> which <u>add/subtract</u> to give <u>9x or 3x</u>

$(3x\quad 2)(x\quad 3)$ <u>multiplies</u> to give <u>9x and 2x</u> which <u>add/subtract</u> to give <u>11x or ⑦x</u>

   So $(3x\quad 2)(x\quad 3)$ is the combination that gives b = 7, (give or take a +/−)

5) <u>Now fill in the +/− signs</u> so that the combination will add/subtract to give +7 (=b).
   Clearly it must be +3 and −2 which gives rise to +9x and -2x.
   So the final brackets are: <u>$(3x - 2)(x + 3)$</u>

6) <u>As an ESSENTIAL check, EXPAND the brackets</u> out again to make sure they give the original equation:
   $(3x - 2)(x + 3) =\ 3x^2 + 9x - 2x - 6\ =\ \underline{3x^2 + 7x - 6}$

7) The last step is to get <u>THE SOLUTIONS TO THE EQUATION</u>: $(3x - 2)(x + 3)=0$
   which you do <u>by separately putting each bracket = 0</u> :
      i.e. $(3x - 2) = 0\ \Rightarrow\ \underline{x = 2/3}$ $(x + 3) = 0\ \Rightarrow\ \underline{x = -3}$
   Don't forget that last step. <u>Again, it's the difference</u> between
   <u>SOLVING THE EQUATION</u> and merely <u>factorising</u> it.

It's not scary — just think of it as brackets giving algebra a hug...

Actually, don't 'cause that won't really help you in the Exam. What will help is learning the 7 steps for solving quadratics by factorising — both for 'a = 1' and 'a ≠ 1'. And then answering these questions:

1) Solve these by the factorising method:
a) $x^2 + 5x - 24 = 0$ b) $x^2 - 6x + 9 = 16$ c) $(x + 3)^2 - 3 = 13$ d) $5x^2 - 17x - 12 = 0$

Extended   Extended   Extended

The Quadratic Formula

The solutions to any quadratic equation $ax^2 + bx + c = 0$ are given by this formula:

$$x = \frac{-b \pm \sqrt{b^2 - 4ac}}{2a}$$

<u>LEARN THIS FORMULA</u> — If you can't learn it, there's no way you'll be able to use it in the Exam, even if they give it to you. Using it should, in principle, be quite straightforward. As it turns out though there are quite a few pitfalls, so <u>TAKE HEED of these crucial details</u>:

Using The Quadratic Formula

1) Always write it down in stages as you go. Take it nice and slowly — any fool can rush it and get it wrong, but there's no marks for being a clot.

2) <u>MINUS SIGNS</u>. Throughout the whole of algebra, minus signs cause untold misery <u>because people keep forgetting them</u>. In this formula, there are two minus signs that people keep forgetting: <u>the -b and the -4ac</u>.

   The -4ac causes particular problems <u>when either 'a' or 'c' is negative</u>, because it makes the -4ac effectively +4ac — <u>so learn to spot it as a HAZARD before it happens</u>.

   > WHENEVER YOU GET A MINUS SIGN, <u>THE ALARM BELLS SHOULD ALWAYS RING!</u>

3) Remember you <u>divide ALL of the top line by 2a</u>, not just half of it.

4) Don't forget it's <u>2a</u> on the bottom line, not just a. This is another common mistake.

Example:
"Find the solutions of $3x^2 + 7x = 1$ to 2 decimal places."

The mention of decimal places in Exam questions is a <u>very big clue</u> to use the formula rather than trying to factorise it!

Method:

1) First get it into the form <u>$ax^2 + bx + c = 0$</u>: $3x^2 + 7x - 1 = 0$

2) Then carefully identify a, b and c: <u>a = 3,   b = 7,   c = -1</u>

3) Put these values into the quadratic formula and <u>write down each stage</u>:

$$x = \frac{-b \pm \sqrt{b^2 - 4ac}}{2a} = \frac{-7 \pm \sqrt{7^2 - 4 \times 3 \times -1}}{2 \times 3} = \frac{-7 \pm \sqrt{49 + 12}}{6}$$

$$= \frac{-7 \pm \sqrt{61}}{6} = \frac{-7 \pm 7.81}{6} = 0.1350 \text{ or } -2.468$$

So to 2 DP, the solutions are: <u>x = 0.14 or -2.47</u>

4) Finally, <u>as a check</u> put these values back into the <u>original equation</u>:
   E.g. for x = 0.1350: $3 \times 0.135^2 + 7 \times 0.135 = 0.999675$, which is 1, as near as...

Enough number crunches? Now it's time to work on your quads...

Learn the <u>4 crucial details</u> and the <u>4 steps of the method</u> for using the Quadratic Formula, then turn over and write them all down. Done it? Now it's time to practice your mad new skillz with these handy questions...

1) Find the solutions of these equations (to 2 DP) using the Quadratic Formula:
   a) $x^2 + 10x - 4 = 0$ b) $3x^2 - 3x = 2$ c) $(2x + 3)^2 = 15$

Completing the Square

$$x^2 + 12x - 5 = (x + 6)^2 - 41$$

The SQUARE...   ...COMPLETED

Solving Quadratics by 'Completing The Square'

This is quite a clever way of solving quadratics, but it's perhaps a bit confusing at first.
The name 'Completing the Square' doesn't help — it's called that because you basically:

1) Write down a <u>SQUARED</u> bracket, and then

2) Stick a number on the end to '<u>COMPLETE</u>' it.

It's quite easy if you learn all the steps — some of them aren't all that obvious.

Any idea what's next?

Nope, not a clue.

Method:

1) As always, <u>REARRANGE THE QUADRATIC INTO THE STANDARD FORMAT:</u>
   $$ax^2 + bx + c = 0$$

2) <u>If 'a' is not 1 then divide the whole equation by 'a' to make sure it is!</u>

3) Now <u>WRITE OUT THE INITIAL BRACKET:</u> $(x + b/2)^2$

   NB: <u>THE NUMBER IN THE BRACKET</u> is always <u>HALF THE (NEW) VALUE OF 'b'</u>

4) <u>MULTIPLY OUT THE BRACKETS</u> and <u>COMPARE TO THE ORIGINAL</u>
   to find what extra is needed, and add or subtract the adjusting amount.

Example:

"Express $x^2 - 6x - 7 = 0$ as a completed square, and hence solve it."

The equation is already in the standard form and 'a' = 1, so:

1)   The coefficient of x is -6, so the squared brackets must be: $(x - 3)^2$

2)   <u>Square out the brackets:</u> $x^2 - 6x + 9$, <u>and compare</u> to the original: $x^2 - 6x - 7$.
     To make it like the original equation it needs -16 on the end, hence we get:

$$(x - 3)^2 - 16 = 0 \text{ as the alternative version of } x^2 - 6x - 7 = 0$$

Don't forget though, we wish to <u>SOLVE</u> this equation, which entails these 3 special steps:

1)   <u>Take the 16 over</u> to get: $(x - 3)^2 = 16$.

2)   Then <u>SQUARE ROOT BOTH SIDES:</u> $(x - 3) = \pm 4$ <u>AND DON'T FORGET THE</u> $\pm$

3)   <u>Take the 3 over</u> to get: $x = \pm 4 + 3$ <u>so x = 7 or -1</u>

...but, if a square's not complete, is it really a square...?

Deep. Go over this carefully, 'cos it's pretty gosh darn confusing at first. Learn the <u>4 steps</u> for
completing the square and the <u>3 special steps</u> for <u>solving the equation</u>. Then flex your brain with these...

1)   Find the solutions of these equations (to 2 DP) by completing the square:
     a) $x^2 + 10x - 4 = 0$ b) $3x^2 - 3x = 2$ c) $(2x + 3)^2 = 15$

Extended

Extended

Extended

Functions

A function is really just another way of writing an equation.
Instead of writing an <u>equation</u> like <u>y = 5x + 2</u>, you can write a <u>function</u> like <u>f(x) = 5x + 2</u> or <u>f: x → 5x + 2</u>.
<u>Functions</u> can look a bit scary-mathsy, but they don't involve anything more difficult than a bit of <u>rearranging</u>.

Evaluating Functions

This is easy — just shove the numbers into the function and you're away.

<u>EXAMPLE:</u>   "If $f(x) = x^2 - x + 7$, find f(3)."

<u>ANSWER:</u> $f(3) = 3^2 - 3 + 7 = 9 - 3 + 7 = \underline{13}$

Combining Functions

This is a bit more tricky. You might get a question with two functions, e.g. f(x) and g(x).
Then f(g(x)) and fg(x) both mean <u>exactly the same</u> — <u>replace</u> the <u>x</u> in f(x) with the <u>whole function</u> g(x).

<u>EXAMPLE:</u>   "If $f(x) = 2x - 10$ and $g(x) = -\dfrac{x}{2}$, find: a) fg(x)   b) gf(x)."

<u>ANSWER:</u>   a) $fg(x) = f(-\dfrac{x}{2}) = 2(-\dfrac{x}{2}) - 10 = \underline{-x - 10}$

              b) $gf(x) = g(2x - 10) = -\left(\dfrac{2x - 10}{2}\right) = -(x - 5) = \underline{5 - x}$

> Another way to think of this is that you have to do the function closest to x first. So for fg(x), you do g first, then f.

Inverse Functions

The <u>inverse</u> of a function f(x) is another function, $f^{-1}(x)$, which <u>reverses</u> f(x).
Finding the inverse of a function is only slightly fiddly. Here's the <u>method</u>:

1)   Write out the equation <u>x = f(y)</u>   f(y) is just the expression f(x), but with y's instead of x's

2)   <u>Rearrange</u> the equation to <u>make y the subject</u>. This gives you the equation $y = f^{-1}(x)$.

<u>EXAMPLE:</u> "If $f(x) = \dfrac{12 + x}{3}$, find $f^{-1}(x)$."

<u>ANSWER:</u> 1)   Write out x = f(y): $x = \dfrac{12 + y}{3}$

           2)   Rearrange to make y the subject: $3x = 12 + y \Rightarrow y = 3x - 12$

               So $f^{-1}(x) = \underline{3x - 12}$

You can check your answer by seeing if $f^{-1}(x)$ does reverse f(x): e.g. $f(9) = \dfrac{21}{3} = 7$, $f^{-1}(7) = 21 - 12 = 9$

That page has really put the 'fun' into 'functions'...

Sorry, that joke just had to be made. This is another topic where practice really does make perfect. Start here:

1) If $f(x) = 5x - 1$, $g(x) = 8 - 2x$ and $h(x) = x^2 + 3$, find:
    a) f(4)   b) h(−2)   c) gf(x)   d) fh(x)   e) gh(−3)   f) hf(2)   g) $f^{-1}(x)$ h) $g^{-1}(f(x))$

Inequalities

Inequalities aren't <u>half as difficult as they look</u>. Once you've learned the tricks involved, most of the algebra for them is <u>identical to ordinary equations</u>.

The Inequality Symbols:

> means '<u>Greater than</u>' $\geq$ means '<u>Greater than or equal to</u>'
< means '<u>Less than</u>' $\leq$ means '<u>Less than or equal to</u>'

<u>REMEMBER</u>, the one at the <u>BIG</u> end is <u>BIGGEST</u>

so   x > 4   and   4 < x   both say: '<u>x is greater than 4</u>'

Algebra With Inequalities

The thing to remember here is that <u>inequalities are just like regular equations</u> in the sense that all the normal rules of algebra apply <u>WITH ONE BIG EXCEPTION</u>:

$5x < x + 2$
$5x = x + 2$

Whenever you MULTIPLY OR DIVIDE BY A <u>NEGATIVE NUMBER</u>, you must <u>FLIP THE INEQUALITY SIGN</u>.

Three Important Examples

I > All of you.

1) Solve $5x < 6x + 2$

The equivalent equation is $5x = 6x + 2$, which is easy — and so is the inequality:

First subtract 6x from both sides: $5x - 6x < 2$ which gives $-x < 2$
Then divide both sides by -1:   <u>$x > -2$</u> (i.e. x is greater than -2)
(NOTE: The < has flipped around into a >, because we divided by a negative number)

2) Find all integer values of x where $-4 \leq x < 1$

This type of expression is <u>very common</u> — <u>you must learn them in this way</u>:
'x is between -4 and +1, possibly equal to -4 but never equal to +1'.
(Obviously the answers are <u>-4, -3, -2, -1, 0</u> (but not 1))

3) Find the range of values of x where $x^2 \leq 25$

The trick here is: <u>Don't forget the negative values</u>.

Square-rooting both sides gives $x \leq 5$. However, this is <u>only half the story</u>,

because $-5 \leq x$ is also true. There is little alternative but to simply learn this:

$x^2 \leq 25$ gives the solution $-5 \leq x \leq 5$,
(x is between -5 and 5, possibly equal to either).
$x^2 \geq 36$ gives the solution $x \leq -6$ or $6 \leq x$
(x is 'less than or equal to -6' or 'greater than or equal to +6').

I saw you flip the inequality sign — how rude...

Learn all of this page including the <u>three important examples</u>, then turn over and write it all down. Now try these:
1) Solve this inequality: $4x + 3 \leq 6x + 7$
2) Find all integer values of p, such that a) $p^2 < 49$ b) $-20 < 4p \leq 17$

<u>Linear Programming</u>

Linear programming is a way to solve <u>simultaneous inequalities</u>. It's a bit trickier than solving simultaneous equations because there are <u>lots of possible solutions</u> — using a <u>graph</u> helps you to find the <u>best solution</u>. LP questions tend to be worth a lot of marks — so I'd say it's worth learning how to tackle them.

<u>LINEAR PROGRAMMING QUESTIONS ALL FOLLOW THE SAME PATTERN</u> and it's really important you realise just how <u>REPETITIVE</u> they are. The <u>THREE SEPARATE STAGES</u> that occur in <u>ALL</u> linear programming questions are best illustrated by a typical example. Every step of the following method needs to be <u>LEARNT</u>:

1) Convert the Sentences into Inequalities

The local "Supplies 'n' Vittals" have two top sellers: "<u>Froggatt's Lumpy Sprout Ketchup</u>" and "<u>Froggatt's Bone-tingling Fireball Soup</u>". The sales of these products are limited by the following factors:

1) A shortage of sprouts has meant <u>total sales of the Ketchup are rationed to 200</u> bottles per month.

2) The Health Department has <u>limited the combined sales of these two products to 250 items per month</u>.

3) Froggatt's themselves, ever keen to preserve their more traditional health products, insist that <u>all retailers must sell at least as much Ketchup as Bone-tingling Soup</u>.

Using K to represent the number of bottles of Lumpy Sprout Ketchup sold and S to represent the number of tins of Bone-tingling Fireball Soup, write down three inequalities.

<u>ANSWER</u> 1) Surely it's pretty obvious that the first condition is simply written: $K \leq 200$

2) Neither is it difficult to convert the second sentence into: $K + S \leq 250$

3) A little trickier but still quite straightforward: $K \geq S$

Technically, there are two more conditions — you can't sell a negative number of items, so $K \geq 0$ and $S \geq 0$.

This set of <u>THREE CONDITIONS</u> is a <u>key feature of Linear Programming questions</u>, and the method to turn them into equations <u>isn't so mysterious</u>, it just needs to be <u>LEARNT</u>.

If you look at the <u>mathematical expressions</u> and the <u>underlined parts</u> of the corresponding statements, <u>it's really quite easy</u> to see how you turn one into the other.

2) Draw The Graphs

Once you've got your inequalities, you need to draw them on a graph.

The general method for graphing inequalities goes like this:

> 1) <u>CONVERT each INEQUALITY to an EQUATION</u>
> by simply putting an '=' in place of the '<' or '>'
>
> 2) <u>DRAW THE GRAPH FOR EACH EQUATION</u>
> Use a solid line if the inequality is '$\leq$' or '$\geq$',
> and a dotted line if it's '<' or '>'.
>
> 3) <u>Work out WHICH SIDE of each line you want</u>
>
> 4) <u>SHADE OUT the UNWANTED AREAS of the graph</u>

The first couple of steps are pretty easy. Continuing with the example above:

1) <u>CONVERT EACH INEQUALITY TO AN EQUATION</u>:
The inequalities become $K = 200$, $K + S = 250$ and $K = S$.

2) <u>DRAW THE GRAPH FOR EACH EQUATION</u>
(see p39 if you need a reminder about drawing graphs)

Linear Programming

Shading The Region

So, now you've got a beautiful graph. Next it's the fiddly bit...

3) **WORK OUT WHICH SIDE OF EACH LINE YOU WANT**
Pick a point that's not on any of the lines, e.g. (150, 200).
Substitute the values of K and S at that point into each
inequality and see if this makes the inequality <u>true</u> or <u>false</u>.

> If K = 150, S = 200:
>
> K ≤ 200 gives 150 ≤ 200 which is <u>true</u>.
> This means (150, 200) is on the <u>correct</u> side of the line.
>
> K + S ≤ 250 gives 350 ≤ 250 which is <u>false</u>.
> So (150, 200) is on the <u>wrong side</u> of this line.
>
> K ≥ S gives 150 > 200 which is <u>false</u>.
> So (150, 200) is on the <u>wrong side</u> of this line too.

The <u>solid lines</u> mean the solution <u>includes</u> the points on the line. If your inequality had a < or > instead of a ≤ or ≥, you'd draw a <u>dotted line</u>.

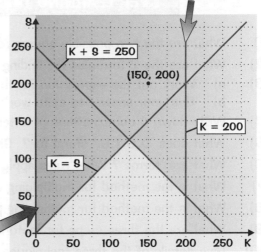

4) **SHADE OUT THE REGION YOU DON'T WANT**
You want to shade out all these areas:
  – <u>right of K = 200</u> (because (150, 200) <u>isn't</u> on this side)
  – <u>above K + S = 250</u> (because (150, 200) <u>is</u> on this side)
  – <u>above K = S</u> (because (150, 200) <u>is</u> on this side).

The points in the unshaded area satisfy all three inequalities. All the points in the region with
integer coordinates represent possible amounts of soup and ketchup that could be sold.

3) Find the Optimum Point

The question always ends up mentioning some quantity (usually INCOME), which has to be OPTIMISED
(i.e. made <u>as big or as small as possible</u>) within the shaded region:

> <u>Example</u>: "The prices of these products are <u>£2 per bottle of Lumpy Sprout Ketchup</u>,
> and <u>£1.50 per tin of Bone-tingling Fireball Soup</u>. Find the maximum
> possible <u>income</u>, and say how many of each will be sold per month."

From this sort of information you should never have
any real trouble writing a simple equation like this one: "<u>Income = 2K + 1.5S</u>"

The optimum point will always be at <u>one corner</u> of the <u>unshaded bit</u> of the graph,
so once you've got your equation for income (or whatever), all you need to do is:

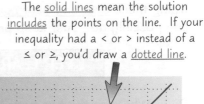

1) Find the coordinates of each corner of the unshaded area.
In the example, they're at (0, 0), (200, 0), (200, 50) and (125, 125).

2) Stick each pair of coordinates in the formula:
(2 × 0) + (1.5 × 0) = 0   (2 × 200) + (1.5 × 0) = 400
(2 × 200) + (1.5 × 50) = 475   (2 × 125) + (1.5 × 125) = 437.50

3) The point that gives the highest value (or the lowest, depending on what you're looking for) represents the
<u>optimum combination</u>. In this case it's to sell <u>200 bottles of Ketchup</u> and <u>50 tins of Soup</u> and take <u>£475</u>.

Graphing inequalities is a shady business...

LEARN EVERY STEP OF THE METHOD on these two pages. Then <u>turn over and see what you know</u>.

1) Practise the above example until you can do the whole thing with contemptuous ease.

2) Do the question again but with these new figures: The Bone-Tingling Soup goes up to £3 per tin, and the
total monthly sales may now go up to 300 items.

Revision Summary

Section Four is the really nasty one — grisly grimsdike algebra. But grisly or not, you still have to learn it. Here's another set of questions to test what you know. Don't forget, you've got to keep trying these <u>over and over again</u>. Making sure that you can do these questions is the <u>best revision</u> you can possibly do. Just keep practising till you can glide through them all like a turtle or something.

KEEP LEARNING THESE BASIC FACTS UNTIL YOU KNOW THEM

1) What are the two possible square roots of 9?

2) What are the 2 formulas for finding the nth term of a sequence?

3) a) Work out the expression for the nth term in this sequence: −1, 5, 11, 17, 23, ...
   b) Use your answer to a) to work out the 10th term in the sequence.

4) Write down 4 combinations of letters that regularly catch people out in algebra.

5) What does 'D.O.T.S.' stand for? Give two examples of it.

6) What are 'terms'? What rules apply to them?

7) What is the method for multiplying out brackets such as $3(2x + 4)$?

8) What is the method for multiplying pairs of brackets? What about squared brackets?

9) What are the three steps for factorising expressions such as $12x^2y^3z + 15x^3yz^2$?

10) Give details of the three techniques for doing algebraic fractions, with examples.

11) 'To find y you double x and add 4.' Write this as a formula.

12) What are the six steps for solving equations or rearranging formulas? What's the 7th step?

13) Jacob stocks the tuck shop with chocolate bars each week. Last week he spent £4.20 buying 6 chocolate bars and 3 pints of milk for his mum. This week he spent £5.32 on 10 chocolate bars and 2 pints of milk (for his mum again). His receipts weren't itemised and he needs to know how much money to take back from the tuck shop for the chocolate bars (all the chocolate bars are the same price).
   a) Write simultaneous equations for Jacob's two receipts.
   b) Solve the equations to calculate how much money Jacob is owed.

14) List the three key features of both direct proportion and inverse proportion.

15) Give three examples of the sort of statements that are involved in the subject of 'variation'?

16) What does 'factorising a quadratic' mean you have to do?

17) What check should you do to make sure you've done it right?

18) What difference does it make when factorising a quadratic if 'a' is not 1?

19) How exactly do you get solutions to a quadratic equation once you've factorised it?

20) Write down the formula for solving quadratics.

21) What are the three main pitfalls that catch people out with the quadratic formula?

22) What are the four main steps for turning a quadratic into a 'completed square'?

23) If $f(x)$ and $g(x)$ are functions, what do you do to get the combined function $fg(x)$?

24) How do you find the inverse of a function $f(x)$?

25) What do you need to do if you divide an inequality by a negative number?

26) What are the three main stages of a linear programming question?

27) What is the four-stage method for graphical inequalities?

28) What does it mean if the graph of an inequality is drawn as a dotted line?

29) What is the meaning of life? Why are we here? And why do we have to do so much algebra?

Symmetry

After you've finished this page, remind me that I need to pop out and buy some milk. There'll be none left for my breakfast otherwise. Anyway, sorry, symmetry... Right, yes, there are THREE types of symmetry:

1) Line Symmetry

This is where you can draw a MIRROR LINE (or more than one) across a picture and both sides will fold exactly together.

| 2 LINES OF SYMMETRY | 1 LINE OF SYMMETRY | 1 LINE OF SYMMETRY | 3 LINES OF SYMMETRY | NO LINES OF SYMMETRY | 1 LINE OF SYMMETRY |

2) Plane Symmetry

> Plane symmetry is all to do with 3-D SOLIDS. Whereas flat shapes can have mirror lines, solid 3-D objects can have planes of symmetry.

A plane mirror surface can be drawn through many regular solids, but the shape must be exactly the same on both sides of the plane (i.e. mirror images), like these are:

Planes of Symmetry

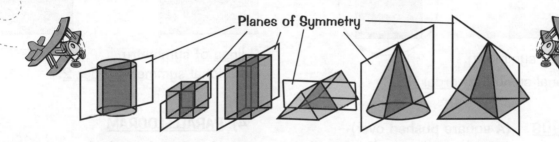

The shapes drawn here all have many more planes of symmetry but there's only one drawn in for each shape, because otherwise it would all get really messy and you wouldn't be able to see anything.

3) Rotational Symmetry

This is where you can rotate the shape into different positions that look exactly the same.

If a shape has only 1 position, you can either say 'order 1 symmetry' or 'no rotational symmetry'

   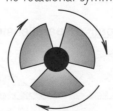 

| Order 1 | Order 2 | Order 2 | Order 3 | Order 4 |

I'd like to say I'm a fan of this topic, but I'm not very good at line...

A nice easy page for you there. Get it learnt and it'll help you on the way to getting a nice symmetrical A in your Exam. Right then,

1) Find the lines of symmetry and order of rotational symmetry for: H   N   E   Y   M   S   T
2) Work out the other planes of symmetry for the 3D solids above.

Triangles and Quadrilaterals

— make sure you know them all.

Three-sided Shapes — Triangles
(just in case you didn't know...)

1) **EQUILATERAL Triangle**

3 lines of symmetry.
Rotational symmetry order 3.

2) **RIGHT-ANGLED Triangle**

No symmetry unless the angles are 45°.

3) **ISOSCELES Triangle**
2 sides equal
2 angles equal

1 line of symmetry.
No rotational symmetry.

Four-sided Shapes — Quadrilaterals

1) **SQUARE**

 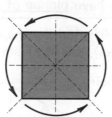

4 lines of symmetry.
Rotational symmetry order 4.

2) **RECTANGLE**

2 lines of symmetry.
Rotational symmetry order 2.

3) **RHOMBUS** (A square pushed over)
(It's also a diamond)

 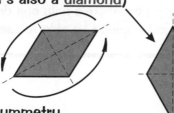

2 lines of symmetry.
Rotational symmetry order 2.

4) **PARALLELOGRAM**
(A rectangle pushed over —
two pairs of parallel sides)

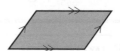

NO lines of symmetry.
Rotational symmetry order 2.

5) **TRAPEZIUM** (One pair of parallel sides)

Only the isosceles trapezium has a line of symmetry.
None have rotational symmetry.

6) **KITE**

1 line of symmetry.
No rotational symmetry.

Rhombus facts: 4 sides, 2 lines of symmetry, Gemini, peanut allergy...

Learn everything on this page. Then turn over and write down all the details that you can remember.
Then try again. It's as simple as that. Then you can play with the kite. Indoors though — it's new.

Regular Polygons

A <u>polygon</u> is a <u>many-sided shape</u>. A <u>regular</u> polygon is one where all the <u>sides</u> and <u>angles</u> are the same. The regular polygons are a never-ending series of shapes with some fancy features.

You Need to Know These Polygons

EQUILATERAL TRIANGLE
<u>3 sides</u>
<u>3 lines</u> of symmetry
Rot^{nl} symm. <u>order 3</u>

SQUARE
<u>4 sides</u>
<u>4 lines</u> of symmetry
Rot^{nl} symm. <u>order 4</u>

REGULAR PENTAGON
<u>5 sides</u>
<u>5 lines</u> of symmetry
Rot^{nl} symm. <u>order 5</u>

REGULAR HEXAGON
<u>6 sides</u>
<u>6 lines</u> of symmetry
Rot^{nl} symm. <u>order 6</u>

REGULAR HEPTAGON
<u>7 sides</u>
<u>7 lines</u> of symmetry
Rot^{nl} symm. <u>order 7</u>

REGULAR OCTAGON
<u>8 sides</u>
<u>8 lines</u> of symmetry
Rot^{nl} symm. <u>order 8</u>

You also need to know the <u>next two</u>, but I'm not drawing them for you. <u>Learn their names</u>:

REGULAR NONAGON
<u>9 sides</u>, etc. etc.

REGULAR DECAGON
<u>10 sides</u>, etc. etc.

Polygons Have Interior and Exterior Angles

1) Exterior Angles

2) Interior Angles

3) This angle is always the same as the Exterior Angles.

4) Each sector triangle is <u>ISOSCELES</u>.

Note — the two SUM formulas above work for **any** polygons, not just regular ones.

There are 4 formulas to learn:

$$\text{EXTERIOR ANGLE} = \frac{360°}{n}$$

$$\text{INTERIOR ANGLE} = 180° - \text{EXTERIOR ANGLE}$$

$$\text{SUM OF EXTERIOR ANGLES} = 360°$$

$$\text{SUM OF INTERIOR ANGLES} = (n - 2) \times 180°$$

(n is the number of sides)

Regular Polygons have Loads of Symmetry

1) The pentagon shown here has <u>only 3 different angles</u> in the whole diagram.

2) This is <u>typical of regular polygons</u>. They display an amazing amount of symmetry.

3) With a regular polygon, if two angles <u>look</u> the same, they <u>will be</u>. That's not a rule you should normally apply in geometry, and anyway you'll need to <u>prove</u> they're equal.)

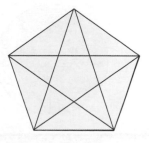

EXCLUSIVE: Heptagon lottery winner says "I'm still just a regular guy"...

Lots to learn on this page. But as long as you're familiar with the word regular, you're half way there.

1) What is a regular polygon?

2) Name the first six of them.

3) Work out the two key angles for a regular pentagon

4) And for a 12-sided regular polygon.

5) Draw a regular pentagon and a regular hexagon and put in all their lines of symmetry.

Areas

Yes, I thought I could detect some groaning when you realised that this is a page of formulas that you need to learn. Well, I'm afraid it's tough — the sooner you get on with it, the <u>sooner</u> you'll have them learnt.

You must LEARN these Formulas:

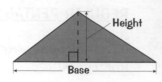

<u>Area of triangle</u> = ½ × base × vertical height

Note that the <u>height</u> must always be the <u>vertical height</u>, not the sloping height.

(Trigonometry is covered on p90-94)

The alternative formula is this:
<u>Area of triangle</u> = ½ ab sin C

$$A = ½ × b × h_v$$

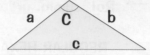

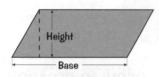

$$\frac{\text{Area of}}{\text{parallelogram}} = \text{base × vertical height}$$

$$A = b × h_v$$

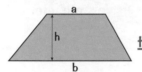

$$\frac{\text{Area of}}{\text{trapezium}} = \frac{\text{average of}}{\text{parallel sides}} × \frac{\text{distance}}{\text{between them}}$$

$$A = ½ × (a + b) × h$$

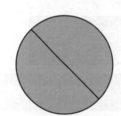

<u>Area of circle</u> = π × (radius)² $A = π × r^2$

<u>Circumference</u> = π × diameter $C = π × D$

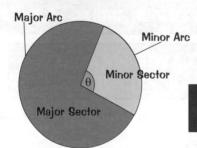

Major Arc
Minor Arc
Minor Sector
θ
Major Sector

$$\underline{\text{Area of Sector}} = \frac{θ}{360} × \text{Area of full Circle}$$ (Pretty obvious really isn't it?)

$$\underline{\text{Length of Arc}} = \frac{θ}{360} × \text{Circumference of full Circle}$$ (Obvious again, no?)

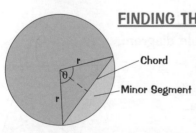

r
Chord
θ
Minor Segment
r

<u>**FINDING THE AREA OF A SEGMENT**</u> is OK if you know the formulas:

1) Find the <u>area of the sector</u> using the above formula.

2) Find the area of the triangle, then <u>subtract it</u> from the sector's area. You can do this using the '½ ab sin C' formula for the area of the triangle which becomes: ½ r²sin θ.

<u>*Pi r not square — pi are round. Pi are tasty...*</u>

Right, nothing too scary on this page — just a load of formulas to learn. Plain and simple. And once you've got them all learned, have a crack at this question.

1) <u>Find the perimeter and area of this shape.</u> As you should certainly expect for any Exam question on area, you will need to make use of <u>Pythagoras and/or trigonometry</u> to solve this one. (See p89-91.)

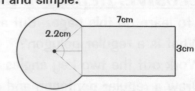

2.2cm   7cm   3cm

Surface Area and Volume

It's pretty simple to work out the surface area of a 3D shape — you just need to imagine the surface <u>unfolded</u>.

Surface Area and Nets

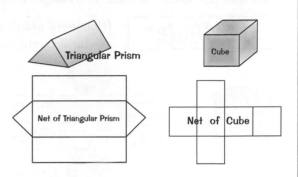

1) <u>SURFACE AREA</u> only applies to solid 3D objects, and it is simply <u>the total area</u> of all the <u>outer surfaces</u> added together. If you were painting it, it's all the bits you'd paint.
2) <u>A NET</u> is just <u>A SOLID SHAPE FOLDED OUT FLAT</u>.
3) So obviously: <u>SURFACE AREA OF SOLID = AREA OF NET</u>.

1) Cuboid (rectangular block)

(This is also known as a 'rectangular prism' — see below to understand why.)

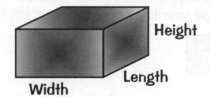

Volume of Cuboid = length × width × height

$$V = L \times W \times H$$

(The other word for volume is <u>CAPACITY</u>.)

2) Prism

<u>A PRISM</u> is a solid (3D) object which is the same shape all the way through — i.e. it has a <u>CONSTANT AREA OF CROSS-SECTION</u>.

Now, for some reason, not a lot of people know what a prism is, but they come up all the time in Exams, so make sure YOU know.

VOLUME OF PRISM = CROSS-SECTIONAL AREA × LENGTH

Triangular Prism

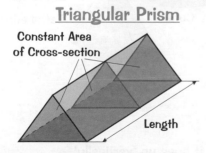

Constant Area of Cross-section

Length

$$V = A \times L$$

As you can see, the formula for the volume of a prism is <u>very simple</u>. The <u>difficult</u> part, usually, is <u>finding the area of the cross-section</u>.

Hexagonal Prism
(a flat one, certainly, but still a prism)

Length

Constant Area of Cross-section

Toblerones — pretty good for prism food...

<u>Learn this page.</u> Then turn over and try to write it all down. <u>Keep trying until you can do it.</u> Then try these out:

1) Name the shapes and find their surface areas and volumes.

a)

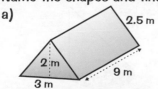

2.5 m
2 m
9 m
3 m

b)

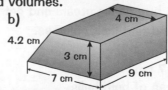

4 cm
4.2 cm
3 cm
7 cm
9 cm

Surface Area and Volume

This page has a great bonus — once you've learnt it you can amaze people by calculating the volume of their ice cream cones. Who says revision isn't fun. I love it. I take Exams just for fun.

3) Cylinder

(Cylinders aren't strictly speaking prisms — but they're so similar it might be useful to think of them as 'circular prisms')

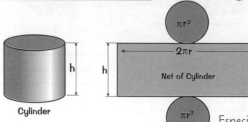

πr^2

$2\pi r$

Net of Cylinder

πr^2

Cylinder

SURFACE AREA of a CYLINDER = $2\pi rh + 2\pi r^2$

VOLUME of a CYLINDER = $\pi r^2 h$

Especially note that <u>the length of the rectangle</u> is equal to the <u>circumference</u> of the circular ends.

4) Sphere

You don't need to learn the formulas for spheres, pyramids or cones — you'll be given them in the Exam if you need them. But you do need to know how to use them, so get practising...

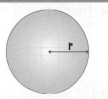

r

Sounds like a load of balls to me

SURFACE AREA of a SPHERE = $4\pi r^2$

VOLUME OF SPHERE = $\frac{4}{3}\pi r^3$

<u>EXAMPLE</u>: The moon has a radius of 1700 km, find its volume.

<u>Ans</u>: $V = \frac{4}{3}\pi r^3 = \frac{4}{3} \times 3.14 \times 1700^3 = 2.1 \times 10^{10}$ km³

(A lot of cheese)

5) Pyramids and Cones

A pyramid is any shape that goes <u>up to a point at the top</u>. Its base can be any shape at all. If the base is a circle then it's called a <u>cone</u> (rather than a circular pyramid).

ℓ

r

curved area of cone   area of circular base

SURFACE AREA of a CONE = $\pi rl + \pi r^2$

You can only use this formula for cones that go straight up ('right cones').

There isn't a formula for surface area of a pyramid (because the shape of the base can vary). If you're asked to find the surface area you'll be given enough information to work it out by drawing a net.

Cone

Tetrahedron

Square-based Pyramid

VOLUME OF PYRAMID = $\frac{1}{3} \times$ BASE AREA $\times$ HEIGHT

VOLUME OF CONE = $\frac{1}{3} \times \pi r^2 \times$ HEIGHT

This surprisingly simple formula is true for any pyramid or cone, whether it goes up 'vertically' (like the three shown here) or off to one side (like the one at the bottom of the page).

No mum, a cone isn't 'just as good' — all the other Pharaohs will laugh at me...

Go on, have a go... Get out there, buy an ice cream and get your ruler out. But first...

1) Name the shapes to the right and find their volumes.

2) A ping pong ball has a diameter of 4 cm.
A tennis ball has a diameter of 7 cm.
Find the volume and surface area of both balls.

a)

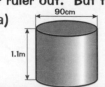

90cm

1.1m

b)

4m

2.2m

Extended

Extended

Congruence and Similarity

Congruence is another ridiculous maths word which sounds really complicated when it's not:
If two shapes are congruent, they are simply <u>the same</u> — the <u>same size</u> and the <u>same shape</u>.
That's all it is. They can however be <u>mirror images</u>.

CONGRUENT
— same size,
same shape

SIMILAR
— same shape,
<u>different size</u>

Note that the angles
are always unchanged

Congruent Triangles — are they or aren't they?

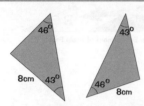

Probably the <u>trickiest area</u> of congruence is deciding whether <u>two triangles</u>, like the ones shown here, are <u>CONGRUENT</u>.

In other words, from the skimpy information given, are the two going to be the same or different. There are **THREE IMPORTANT STEPS**:

1) The Golden Rule is definitely to <u>draw them both</u> in the <u>same orientation</u> — only then can you compare them properly:

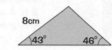 

2) <u>Don't jump to hasty conclusions</u> — although the 8 cm sides are clearly in different positions, it's always possible that <u>both top sides are 8 cm</u>. In this case we can work out that they're <u>not</u> because the angles are different (so they can't be isosceles).

3) Now see if any of these <u>conditions are true</u>. If <u>ONE</u> of the conditions holds, the triangles are <u>congruent</u>.

1)	SSS	three sides are the same
2)	AAS	two angles and a side match up
3)	SAS	two sides and the angle between them match up
4)	RHS	a right angle, the hypotenuse (longest side) and one other side all match up

For two triangles to be congruent, <u>ONE OR MORE</u> of these four conditions must hold.

(If <u>none are true</u>, then you have proof that the triangles <u>aren't congruent</u>.)

Congruence and Transformations

Here's a little bit about <u>transformations</u>. See pages 82-83 for more.

> WHEN A SHAPE IS <u>TRANSLATED</u>, <u>ROTATED</u> OR <u>REFLECTED</u>,
> THE IMAGE IS CONGRUENT TO THE ORIGINAL SHAPE.
> <u>ENLARGEMENTS</u> DON'T FOLLOW THIS RULE.

E.g.

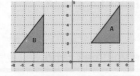

A to B is a <u>translation</u> of $\begin{pmatrix} -8 \\ -1 \end{pmatrix}$.
The lengths and angles
are unchanged, so <u>A is congruent to B</u>.

E.g.

A to B is an <u>enlargement</u> of scale factor 2, and centre (2, 6).

The angles are unchanged but not the lengths, so <u>A is not congruent to B</u>.

Now, where did I put that cup of tea...

Ah there it is over there. Lovely. So here's the bad news — you need to know everything on this page. And the good news — it'll all be great fun. What... you don't believe me? <u>When you think you know it</u>, turn the page over and <u>write it all down</u> from <u>memory</u>, including the sketches and examples.

They're my biscuits. Hands off.

Similarity and Enlargements

You'll be an expert in scale factors after this page — bet you can't wait.

4 Key Features

1) If the <u>Scale Factor is bigger than 1</u> the <u>shape gets bigger</u>.

A to B is an Enlargement, Scale Factor 1½

2) If the <u>Scale Factor is smaller than 1</u> (i.e. a fraction like ½) then the <u>shape gets smaller</u>. (Really this is a reduction, but you still call it <u>an Enlargement, Scale Factor ½</u>)

A to B is an Enlargement of Scale Factor ½

(side margin: Extended)

3) If the <u>Scale Factor is NEGATIVE</u> then the shape pops out the other side of the enlargement centre. If the scale factor is -1, it's exactly the same as a rotation of 180°.

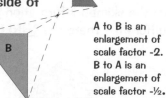

A to B is an enlargement of scale factor -2. B to A is an enlargement of scale factor -½.

(side margin: Extended)

4) The <u>Scale Factor</u> also tells you the <u>relative distance</u> of old points and new points <u>from the Centre of Enlargement</u> — this is <u>very useful for drawing an enlargement</u>, because you can use it to trace out the positions of the new points:

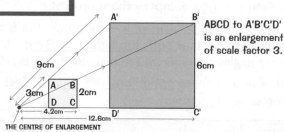

ABCD to A'B'C'D' is an enlargement of scale factor 3.

9cm   6cm
3cm   2cm
4.2cm   12.6cm
THE CENTRE OF ENLARGEMENT

Areas and Volumes of Enlargements

(side margin: Extended)

Ho ho! This little joker catches everybody out. The increase in area and volume is <u>BIGGER</u> than the scale factor.

<u>For example</u>, if the <u>Scale Factor is 2</u>, the lengths are <u>twice as big</u>, each area is <u>4 times</u> as big, and the volume is <u>8 times</u> as big.

The rule is this:

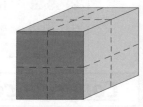

<u>For a SCALE FACTOR N:</u>		<u>Or... expressed AS RATIOS:</u>		
The <u>SIDES</u> are	N times bigger	Lengths	a : b	e.g. 3 : 4
The <u>AREAS</u> are	N² times bigger	Areas	a² : b²	e.g. 9 : 16
The <u>VOLUMES</u> are	N³ times bigger	Volumes	a³ : b³	e.g. 27 : 64
	Simple... but <u>VERY FORGETTABLE</u>			

<u>EXAMPLE</u>:
2 spheres have surface areas of 16 m² and 25 m². Find the ratio of their volumes.

<u>ANS</u>: 16 : 25 is the areas ratio which must be a² : b²,
i.e. $a^2 : b^2 = 16 : 25$
and so $a : b = 4 : 5$
and so $a^3 : b^3 = \underline{64 : 125}$ — the volumes ratio.

Scale factors — they're enough to put the fear of cod in you...

Learn the key features of enlargements, and the rules for area and volume ratios. Then tackle these mackerels:

1) Draw the triangle A(2,1) B(5,2) C(4,4) and enlarge it by a scale factor of -1½, centre the origin. Label the new triangle A' B' C' and give the coordinates of its corners.

2) Two similar cones have volumes of 27 m³ and 64 m³. If the surface area of the smaller one is 36 m², find the surface area of the other one.

Measuring Angles

You might get a question where you need to give the <u>exact value</u> of an angle rather than an estimate. If this happens — <u>DON'T PANIC</u>, just reach for your <u>protractor</u> and follow the advice given below.

Using Protractors

The <u>2 big mistakes</u> that people make with PROTRACTORS:

> 1) <u>Not putting the 0° line at the start position</u>
> 2) <u>Reading from the WRONG SCALE.</u>

These scales won't work.

Two Rules for Getting it Right

1) <u>ALWAYS</u> position the protractor with the <u>bottom edge</u> of it along one of the lines as shown here:

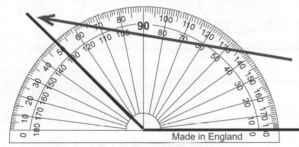

Count in 10° steps from the <u>start line</u> right round to the <u>other one</u> over there.

← Start line

2) <u>COUNT THE ANGLE IN 10° STEPS</u> from the start line right round to the other one.

> <u>DON'T JUST READ A NUMBER OFF THE SCALE</u> — chances are it'll be the <u>WRONG ONE</u> because there are <u>TWO scales to choose from</u>.
>
> The answer here is 130° — NOT 50° — which you will only get right if you start counting 10°, 20°, 30°, 40° etc. from the start line until you reach the other line. You should also <u>estimate</u> it as a check.

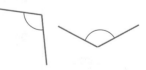

Neither will these.

Acute Angles

<u>SHARP POINTY ONES</u>
(less than 90°)

Obtuse Angles

<u>FLATTER-LOOKING ONES</u>
(between 90° and 180°)

Reflex Angles

<u>ONES THAT BEND BACK ON THEMSELVES</u>
(more than 180°)

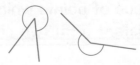

Right Angles

<u>SQUARE CORNERS</u>
(exactly 90°)

Roses are red, tulips are plum, if you were an angle you'd be acute one...

Ho, ho, ho — pretty funny aren't I. Anyway, moving on...

1) LEARN 2 rules for using protractors.
2) LEARN what ACUTE, OBTUSE, REFLEX and RIGHT ANGLES are. Draw one example of each.
3) Use a protractor to accurately draw these angles: a) 35° b) 150° c) 80°

Loci and Constructions

"Loci and constructions — what the monkey is that about" I hear you cry. Well, wonder no more...

Drawing Loci

A <u>LOCUS</u> (another ridiculous maths word) is simply:

> A LINE that shows <u>all the points which fit in with a given rule</u>

Make sure you <u>learn</u> how to do these <u>PROPERLY</u> using a <u>RULER AND COMPASSES</u> as shown.

The locus of points which are '<u>A fixed distance from a given point</u>'

This locus is simply a <u>CIRCLE</u>.

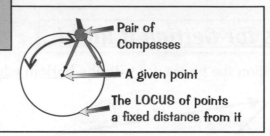

Pair of Compasses

A given point

The LOCUS of points a fixed distance from it

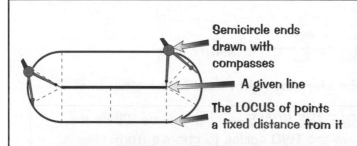

Semicircle ends drawn with compasses

A given line

The LOCUS of points a fixed distance from it

The locus of points which are '<u>A fixed distance from a given line</u>'

This locus is an <u>OVAL SHAPE</u>

It has <u>straight sides</u> (drawn with a <u>ruler</u>) and <u>ends</u> which are <u>perfect semicircles</u> (drawn with <u>compasses</u>).

The locus of points which are '<u>Equidistant from two given lines</u>'

1) Keep the compass setting <u>THE SAME</u> while you make <u>all four marks</u>.

2) Make sure you <u>leave</u> your compass marks <u>showing</u>.

3) You get <u>two equal angles</u> — i.e. this <u>LOCUS</u> is actually an <u>ANGLE BISECTOR</u>.

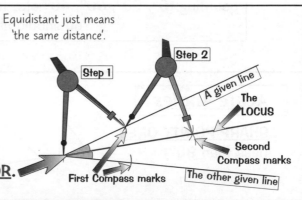

Equidistant just means 'the same distance'.

Step 1   Step 2

A given line

The LOCUS

Second Compass marks

First Compass marks

The other given line

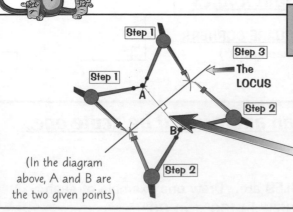

Step 1   Step 1   Step 3

The LOCUS

A

Step 2

B   Step 2

(In the diagram above, A and B are the two given points)

The locus of points which are '<u>Equidistant from two given POINTS</u>'

<u>This LOCUS</u> is all the points which are the <u>same distance</u> from <u>A</u> and <u>B</u>.

This time the locus is actually the <u>PERPENDICULAR BISECTOR</u> of the line joining the two points.

Weird, scary, mutant monkey. Run... RUN...

Loci and Constructions

More on loci and constructions. Don't be alarmed by the floating, body-less hands. They're just there to point out the right diagram at the right time. Just pretend they're <u>regular</u> arrows.

Constructing accurate 60° angles

1) They may well ask you to draw an <u>accurate 60° angle</u>.

2) One place they're needed is for drawing an <u>equilateral triangle</u>.

3) Make sure you <u>follow the method</u> shown in this diagram, and that you can do it <u>entirely from memory</u>.

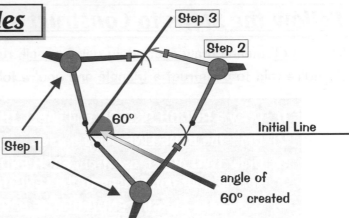

Constructing accurate 90° angles

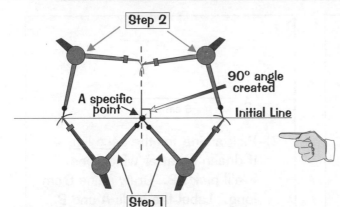

1) They might want you to draw an <u>accurate 90° angle</u>.

2) They won't accept it just done '<u>by eye</u>' or with a ruler — if you want to get the marks, you've got to do it <u>the proper way</u> with <u>compasses</u> like I've shown you here.

3) Make sure you can <u>follow the method</u> shown in this diagram.

Drawing the Perpendicular from a Point to a Line

1) This is similar to the one above but <u>not quite</u> the same — make sure you can do <u>both</u>.

2) Again, they won't accept it just done '<u>by eye</u>' or with a ruler — you've got to do it the <u>proper way</u> with <u>compasses</u>.

3) <u>Learn</u> the diagram.

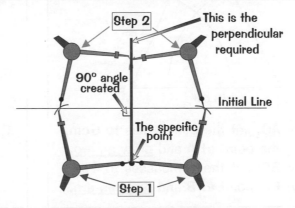

If you're loci, you won't get tested on this stuff...

Haha — I crack myself up. But hilarious jokes aside, make sure you do learn these pages.
Start by covering them up and drawing an example of each of the four loci from memory.
Then draw an equilateral triangle and a square, both with fabulously accurate 60° and 90° angles.
Also, draw a line and a point and construct the perpendicular from the point to the line. Lovely.

Triangle Construction

I just know that you're dying to draw some triangles about now. And that's so weird, because that's exactly what's coming up next in this uber-exciting quest to master maths exams. Spooky.

Follow the Steps to Construct a Triangle

'Construct' means draw accurately using pencil, ruler and compasses.

If you're told to construct a triangle and you're told how long the three sides are, this is what to do.

> 1) Draw a ROUGH SKETCH and LABEL THE LENGTHS of the sides.
> 2) Draw the BASE LINE using a ruler.
> 3) Draw TWO ARCS, one from EACH END of the base line, setting your compasses to the LENGTHS OF THE SIDES.
> 4) Draw lines from the ENDS OF THE BASE LINE to where the TWO ARCS CROSS.

Example:
Construct the triangle ABC where AB = 6 cm, BC = 4 cm, AC = 5 cm.

ANSWER:

Try not to trap anyone inside your triangle. This one was an accident

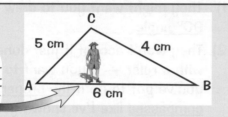

1) Sketch the triangle. Label the corners A, B and C. Label the lengths (AB means the side going from A to B).

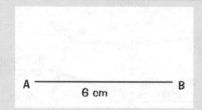

2) Pick a side for the base line — it doesn't matter which one. We'll pick AB. Draw a line 6 cm long. Label the ends A and B.

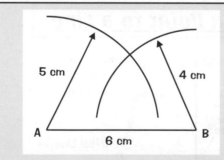

3) For AC, set the compasses to 5 cm, put the point at A and draw an arc. For BC, set the compasses to 4 cm, put the point at B and draw an arc.

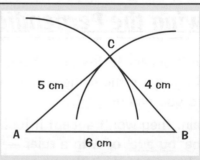

4) Where the arcs cross is the point C. Draw a line from A to C and another line from B to C to finish your triangle.

Compasses at the ready — three, two, one... Construct...

Don't forget to take a pencil, ruler and compasses into the Exam. Or you'll look like a plonker.
1) Construct an equilateral triangle with sides 5 cm.
2) Construct a triangle with sides 3 cm, 4 cm and 5 cm. Check it by measuring the sides.

Section Five — Shapes, Areas and Drawing

Revision Summary

More difficult questions, <u>but just keep reminding yourself that they're the very best revision you can do</u>.
These questions don't ask anything too tricky, just whether or not you've actually <u>learnt</u> all the
<u>basic facts</u> in Section Five. It's really important to keep practising these as often as you can.

KEEP LEARNING THESE BASIC FACTS UNTIL YOU KNOW THEM

1) What two types of symmetry can 2D shapes have?

2) What are regular polygons? Name the first eight.

3) List the special features that regular polygons have.

4) What do you know about their symmetry?

5) Work out the exterior and interior angles for a regular octagon.

6) Write down the formulas for the area of a triangle, parallelogram, trapezium and circle.

7) Clive is re-carpeting his lounge, which is rectangular. The room is 12 m long and 7 m wide.
   The carpet he wants costs £12 per m². How much will it cost Clive to carpet his lounge?

8) Draw a circle and show what an arc, a sector, a segment and a chord are.

9) What is the formula for the length of an arc? Which other formula is similar?

10) What are the three steps needed to find the area of a segment?

11) What is meant by a net? How is it related to surface area?

Aaarrrggghhh...
Run FASTER...

12) What is a prism? Sketch three different ones.

13) Sketch the nets for these shapes:
    a) triangular prism   b) cylinder   c) cube   d) cuboid

14) A confectionery company is designing the packaging for a new brand of biscuits.
    The packaging will be cylindrical, with a diameter of 4 cm and a height of 15 cm.
    Calculate the surface area of the packaging.

15) A juice company makes apple squash in batches of 9000 cm³. The squash is sold
    in cylindrical cans that have a cross-sectional area of 12 cm² and a height of 6 cm.
    How many of these cans can the company fill from one batch of apple squash?

16) What do "congruent" and "similar" mean?

17) What are the rules for deciding if two triangles are congruent or not?

18) Draw a typical enlargement, showing the two important details.

19) What three types of scale factor are there and
    what is the result of enlarging by each?

20) Julie wants a picture enlarging for a new frame.
    Use the diagram to work out the enlargement
    scale factor Julie needs.

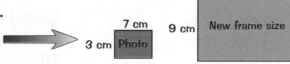

21) Geoff has built a scale model of a garden shed
    that he hopes to supply to garden centres.
    His model is 30 cm wide, 60 cm long and 50 cm high.
    He has used a scale factor of 0.2. Give the width, length and height of the actual sheds.

22) What is a locus?

23) Demonstrate how to accurately draw the bisector of an angle.

24) Demonstrate how to accurately draw the perpendicular bisector of a line.

25) Demonstrate how to draw accurate 60° angles. Draw an accurate equilateral triangle.

26) Demonstrate how to draw accurate 90° angles. Draw an accurate square.

27) Construct a triangle ABC with sides AB = 9 cm, AC = 10 cm and BC = 8 cm.

Section Five — Shapes, Areas and Drawing

Vectors

Three monstrously important things you need to know about <u>vectors</u>. Monsters... Aaaaaarrrggggghhhh...

The Four Notations

The vector shown here can be referred to as:

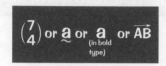

$\binom{7}{4}$ or $\underset{\sim}{a}$ or **a** *(in bold type)* or $\overrightarrow{AB}$

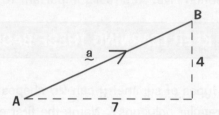

With <u>column vectors</u>, make sure you know:
1)   Which value is which ($x\rightarrow$ and $y\uparrow$).
2)   <u>Positive</u> values mean the vector points <u>up</u> or <u>right</u>, <u>negative</u> values mean it points <u>down</u> or <u>left</u>.

Adding, Subtracting and Multiplying Vectors

Vectors must always be added <u>end to end</u>, so that the <u>arrows</u> don't point <u>against</u> each other.

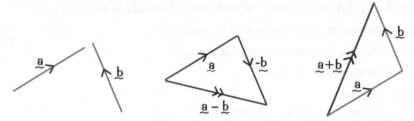

Adding and subtracting <u>**COLUMN VECTORS**</u>, and multiplying them by integers is really easy:

E.g. if $\underset{\sim}{a} = \binom{5}{3}$ and $\underset{\sim}{b} = \binom{-2}{4}$ then $2\underset{\sim}{a} - \underset{\sim}{b} = 2\binom{5}{3} - \binom{-2}{4} = \binom{10}{6} - \binom{-2}{4} = \binom{12}{2}$

A Typical Exam Question

This is a common type of question and it illustrates a very important vector technique:

> To obtain the <u>unknown vector</u> just '<u>get there</u>' by any route <u>made up of known vectors</u>

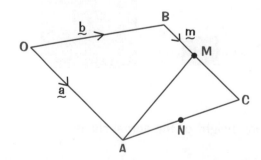

Applying this rule we can easily obtain the following vectors in terms of $\underset{\sim}{a}$, $\underset{\sim}{b}$ and $\underset{\sim}{m}$ (given that M and N are mid points):

$\overrightarrow{AM} = -\underset{\sim}{a} + \underset{\sim}{b} + \underset{\sim}{m}$ (i.e. get there via O and B)

$\overrightarrow{OC} = \underset{\sim}{b} + 2\underset{\sim}{m}$ (i.e. get there via B and M)

$\overrightarrow{AC} = -\underset{\sim}{a} + \underset{\sim}{b} + 2\underset{\sim}{m}$ (A to C via O, B and M)

From numpty to vector king — via R, E, V, I, S, I, O and N...

I know it's dull, but make sure you know the vector basics (and the page doesn't look like a bunch of randomly surfing letters), then real life won't seem so bad. Or real life vectors, which is the next fun page. Now try these:

1)   For the diagram above, express the following in terms of $\underset{\sim}{a}$, $\underset{\sim}{b}$ and $\underset{\sim}{m}$:
   a) $\overrightarrow{MO}$ b) $\overrightarrow{AN}$ c) $\overrightarrow{BN}$ d) $\overrightarrow{NM}$

Vectors

If you get a vector question in the Exam, chances are it'll include a bit about <u>magnitude</u>.

Magnitude of a Vector

$|\vec{AB}|$ means 'the <u>magnitude</u> of $\vec{AB}$'. The magnitude of a vector is just its <u>length</u>.
You can usually work out the length of a vector using good old Pythagoras.

Example 1: "Find $|\vec{CD}|$."

$$\begin{aligned}|\vec{CD}| &= \sqrt{6^2 + 8^2} \\ &= \sqrt{36 + 64} \\ &= \sqrt{100} \\ &= 10\end{aligned}$$

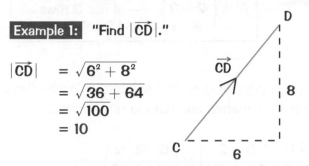

Example 2: "Find the magnitude of the vector $\begin{pmatrix} -7 \\ 10 \end{pmatrix}$."

$$\begin{aligned}\left|\begin{pmatrix} -7 \\ 10 \end{pmatrix}\right| &= \sqrt{(-7)^2 + 10^2} \\ &= \sqrt{49 + 100} \\ &= \sqrt{149} \\ &= 12.21\end{aligned}$$

The Old 'Swimming Across the River' Question

You might have to tackle a slightly trickier 'real-life' vector question. Here's a classic example.

This is a really easy question: You just <u>ADD</u> the two velocity vectors <u>END TO END</u> and draw the <u>RESULTANT VECTOR</u> which shows both the <u>speed</u> and <u>direction</u> of the final course. Simple huh?

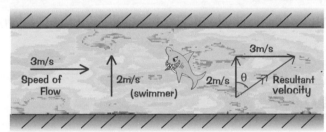

Overall Speed $= \sqrt{3^2 + 2^2}$
$= \sqrt{13} = 3.6 \text{m/s}$
Direction: $\tan\theta = 3 \div 2$
$\theta = \tan^{-1}(1.5) = 56.3°$

You need to use <u>Pythagoras and Trig</u> to find the length and angle, but that's no big deal. Just make sure you LEARN the two methods in this question. The example shown above is bog-standard stuff and you should definitely see it that way, rather than as one random question of which there may be hundreds — there aren't!

Position Vectors are like Coordinates

A <u>position vector</u> tells you where a point is in relation to the <u>origin</u>.
Just like any other vectors, you can <u>add</u>, <u>subtract</u>, <u>multiply</u> and find the <u>magnitude</u> of position vectors.

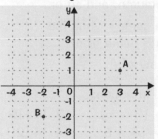

Example:
"Point A has the position vector $\underline{a}$. Point B has the position vector $\underline{b}$. If the position vector of point C is $\underline{c} = \underline{a} + 2\underline{b}$, find the coordinates of point C."

Answer: $\underline{c} = \underline{a} + 2\underline{b} = \begin{pmatrix} 3 \\ 1 \end{pmatrix} + 2\begin{pmatrix} -2 \\ -2 \end{pmatrix} = \begin{pmatrix} 3-4 \\ 1-4 \end{pmatrix} = \begin{pmatrix} -1 \\ -3 \end{pmatrix}$

So the coordinates of C are (-1, -3).

...or if you don't want to be vector king, Queen Vectoria...

Learn how to deal with all these different types of vector questions, then try these:

1) $\vec{AB} = \begin{pmatrix} 2 \\ 5 \end{pmatrix}$ and $\vec{BC} = \begin{pmatrix} -3 \\ 3 \end{pmatrix}$. Find: (a) $|\vec{AB}|$ (b) $|\vec{BC}|$ (c) $|\vec{AC}|$

2) A swimmer is crossing a river. The swimmer swims at 2 m/s, and the river is flowing at a speed of 1 m/s. What angle should the swimmer set off at to ensure he travels straight across the river?

Matrices

A lot of people think <u>matrices</u> are pretty horrific, but the maths you have to do with them is dead easy. It's just a matter of remembering to do it all in the right order...

Three Types of Matrix Calculation

A matrix is just a load of <u>numbers</u>, set out in <u>rows</u> and <u>columns</u>. You normally name them using a bold or underlined capital letter. Make sure you don't get your rows and columns <u>muddled</u>.

$$\underline{A} = \begin{pmatrix} 1 & 3 \\ 2 & -3 \\ -6 & -1 \end{pmatrix} \quad \begin{array}{l} \underline{A} \text{ is a } 3 \times 2 \text{ matrix} \\ \text{— it has } 3 \text{ rows} \\ \text{and } 2 \text{ columns} \end{array}$$

Adding and Subtracting Matrices

You can <u>only</u> add (or subtract) matrices that have <u>the same number</u> of <u>rows</u> and <u>columns</u> as each other.

You add together the numbers that are in the same place in each matrix, and put the result in that position in the answer matrix.

E.g.
$$\begin{pmatrix} 2 & 5 & 0 \\ 9 & -1 & 4 \end{pmatrix} + \begin{pmatrix} 3 & 8 & 2 \\ 4 & 0 & -10 \end{pmatrix} = \begin{pmatrix} 2+3 & 5+8 & 0+2 \\ 9+4 & -1+0 & 4+(-10) \end{pmatrix} = \begin{pmatrix} 5 & 13 & 2 \\ 13 & -1 & -6 \end{pmatrix}$$

$$\begin{pmatrix} 2 & 5 & 0 \\ 9 & -1 & 4 \end{pmatrix} - \begin{pmatrix} 3 & 8 & 2 \\ 4 & 0 & -10 \end{pmatrix} = \begin{pmatrix} 2-3 & 5-8 & 0-2 \\ 9-4 & -1-0 & 4-(-10) \end{pmatrix} = \begin{pmatrix} -1 & -3 & -2 \\ 5 & -1 & 14 \end{pmatrix}$$

Multiplying a Matrix by a Number

To multiply a matrix by a number, you just multiply each individual entry in the matrix by the number.

E.g.
$$4\begin{pmatrix} 1 & -3 \\ 5 & 0 \end{pmatrix} = \begin{pmatrix} 4 & -12 \\ 20 & 0 \end{pmatrix}$$

Multiplying a Matrix by Another Matrix

Let's say your multiplication is $\underline{A} \times \underline{B} = \underline{C}$.

Then:
1) The number of <u>columns</u> in $\underline{A}$ has to be the same as the number of <u>rows</u> in $\underline{B}$.
2) $\underline{C}$ will have the same number of <u>rows</u> as $\underline{A}$, and the same number of <u>columns</u> as $\underline{B}$.
3) If $\underline{A}$ and $\underline{B}$ are square, you can also find $\underline{B} \times \underline{A}$ — but this <u>usually isn't equal</u> to $\underline{A} \times \underline{B}$.

Here's the method to find the entries in the answer matrix $\underline{C}$:

1) Take one row of $\underline{A}$ and one column of $\underline{B}$. Multiply the <u>first entry</u> in the <u>row</u> by the <u>first entry</u> in the <u>column</u>, the <u>second</u> entry in the row by the <u>second</u> entry in the column, and so on.

2) <u>Add</u> together all the <u>products</u> from step one. The total goes in $\underline{C}$, in the <u>same row</u> as the numbers from $\underline{A}$ came from, and the <u>same column</u> as the numbers from $\underline{B}$ came from.

3) <u>Repeat</u> steps 1 and 2 till you've multiplied every column of $\underline{B}$ by every row of $\underline{A}$.

If that sounds a tad confusing, take a look at this example to see the method in action:

E.g.
$$\begin{pmatrix} 1 & 3 \\ 2 & 4 \end{pmatrix}\begin{pmatrix} 0 & 1 & 4 \\ 1 & 3 & 5 \end{pmatrix} = \begin{pmatrix} (1\times0)+(3\times1) & (1\times1)+(3\times3) & (1\times4)+(3\times5) \\ (2\times0)+(4\times1) & (2\times1)+(4\times3) & (2\times4)+(4\times5) \end{pmatrix} = \begin{pmatrix} 3 & 10 & 19 \\ 4 & 14 & 28 \end{pmatrix}$$

"Is that your arrangement of numbers?" — "No, it's my mate Rick's..."

The best way to get the hang of following the rules of matrices and making sure the entries of your answer matrices always end up in the right place is, of course, to practise lots of questions. Start with this one:

1) $\underline{A} = \begin{pmatrix} 4 & 5 \\ -2 & 2 \end{pmatrix}$ $\underline{B} = \begin{pmatrix} -1 & 3 \\ 6 & -9 \end{pmatrix}$ Find:
a) $\underline{A} + \underline{B}$
b) $\underline{B} - \underline{A}$
c) $3\underline{A}$
d) $-\underline{B}$
e) $\underline{A} \times \underline{B}$
f) $\underline{B} \times \underline{A}$

Extended

Matrices

A few special types of matrix to learn about now. A couple of nice, simple ones to start with...

Zero and Identity Matrices

Nothing to these — and you only need to know about the 2×2 versions.

ZERO MATRICES

$\begin{pmatrix} 0 & 0 \\ 0 & 0 \end{pmatrix}$ The 2×2 zero matrix: looks a bit like a button.

1) A zero matrix is (unsurprisingly) a matrix full of zeroes.

2) If you add a matrix **A** to a zero matrix, you get **A**.

3) If you multiply a matrix by a zero matrix, you get a zero matrix.

IDENTITY MATRICES

1) If you multiply a matrix **A** by the identity matrix, you get **A**.

2) The 2×2 identity matrix looks like this: $\begin{pmatrix} 1 & 0 \\ 0 & 1 \end{pmatrix}$

All identity matrices are square, with a diagonal line of ones down the middle, with zeroes everywhere else — but you only need to know about the 2×2. Phew.

Inverses and Determinants

The <u>inverse</u> of the matrix **A** is a matrix $\underline{A}^{-1}$, where $\underline{A} \times \underline{A}^{-1} = \underline{A}^{-1} \times \underline{A}$ = the identity matrix.

To find the inverse of a matrix, first you need to work out a number called the <u>determinant</u>.

For a 2×2 matrix $\begin{pmatrix} a & b \\ c & d \end{pmatrix}$, the DETERMINANT is $ad - bc$.

If the determinant <u>is zero</u>, STOP! The matrix is a <u>singular matrix</u>, which means it <u>doesn't have</u> an inverse.

If the determinant <u>isn't zero</u>, you can carry on and find the inverse.

For a non-singular 2×2 matrix $\begin{pmatrix} a & b \\ c & d \end{pmatrix}$, the INVERSE is $\dfrac{1}{ad - bc}\begin{pmatrix} d & -b \\ -c & a \end{pmatrix}$

Look — that's the determinant on the bottom of the fraction. That's why you can only find the inverse if the determinant isn't zero.

> **Example 1:** "Show that the matrix $\underline{C} = \begin{pmatrix} 3 & 12 \\ 1 & 4 \end{pmatrix}$ is singular."
>
> The determinant of **C** is $(3 \times 4) - (12 \times 1) = 12 - 12 = 0$
> The determinant is zero, so **C** is a singular matrix.

> **Example 2:** "Find the inverse of the matrix $\underline{B} = \begin{pmatrix} 2 & 1 \\ 6 & 5 \end{pmatrix}$."
>
> 1) Find the determinant: $(2 \times 5) - (1 \times 6) = 10 - 6 = 4$
>
> 2) Hooray — the determinant isn't zero, so you can find the inverse: $\underline{B}^{-1} = \dfrac{1}{4}\begin{pmatrix} 5 & -1 \\ -6 & 2 \end{pmatrix}$
>
> 3) Check it really is the inverse:
> $\underline{B}^{-1} \times \underline{B} = \dfrac{1}{4}\begin{pmatrix} 5 & -1 \\ -6 & 2 \end{pmatrix}\begin{pmatrix} 2 & 1 \\ 6 & 5 \end{pmatrix} = \dfrac{1}{4}\begin{pmatrix} (5 \times 2) + (-1 \times 6) & (5 \times 1) + (-1 \times 5) \\ (-6 \times 2) + (2 \times 6) & (-6 \times 1) + (2 \times 5) \end{pmatrix} = \dfrac{1}{4}\begin{pmatrix} 4 & 0 \\ 0 & 4 \end{pmatrix} = \begin{pmatrix} 1 & 0 \\ 0 & 1 \end{pmatrix}$
>
> You could check by multiplying $\underline{B} \times \underline{B}^{-1}$ instead — but it's usually easier to do it this way round and keep that fraction out of the way till the end.

Zeroes are an important feature of matrices — and so are ze columns...

That formula for the inverse of a matrix is a nasty little blighter, but get it learnt and the toughest matrix question will become a doddle. When you think you've learnt and understood everything on this page, try these questions:

1) Find the inverse of each of the following matrices, where possible:　　a) $\begin{pmatrix} 2 & 2 \\ 9 & 5 \end{pmatrix}$　　b) $\begin{pmatrix} -3 & 7 \\ -4 & 9 \end{pmatrix}$　　c) $\begin{pmatrix} 5 & -1 \\ 8 & 3 \end{pmatrix}$

Extended

Extended

Extended

The Four Transformations

T = Translation — ONE Detail
E = Enlargement — TWO Details
R = Rotation — THREE Details
M (for Mirror) = Reflection — ONE Detail

1) Use the word TERM to remember the 4 types.
2) You must always specify all the details for each type. And don't forget to say what type of transformation it is as well.
3) It'll help if you remember which properties remain unchanged in each transformation, too.

1) TRANSLATION

You must specify this ONE detail:

1) The VECTOR OF TRANSLATION $\begin{pmatrix} x \rightarrow \\ \uparrow Y \end{pmatrix}$ (See p78 on vector notation)

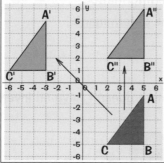

ABC to A'B'C' is a translation of $\begin{pmatrix} -8 \\ 6 \end{pmatrix}$

ABC to A"B"C" is a translation of $\begin{pmatrix} 0 \\ 7 \end{pmatrix}$

All that changes in a translation is the POSITION of the object — everything else remains unchanged.

2) ENLARGEMENT

You must specify these 2 details:

1) The SCALE FACTOR
2) The CENTRE of Enlargement

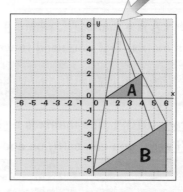

From A to B is an enlargement of scale factor 2, and centre (2,6)

From B to A is an enlargement of scale factor ½ and centre (2,6)

The ANGLES of the object and RATIOS of the lengths remain unchanged. The ORIENTATION is unchanged unless the scale factor is negative.

3) ROTATION

You must specify these 3 details:

1) ANGLE turned
2) DIRECTION (Clockwise or...)
3) CENTRE of Rotation

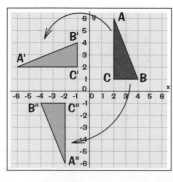

ABC to A'B'C' is a Rotation of 90°, anticlockwise, ABOUT the origin.

ABC to A"B"C" is a Rotation of half a turn (180°), clockwise, ABOUT the origin.

The only things that change in a rotation are the POSITION and the ORIENTATION of the object. Everything else remains unchanged.

4) REFLECTION

You must specify this ONE detail:

1) The MIRROR LINE

A to B is a reflection in the y-axis.

A to C is a reflection in the line y = x.

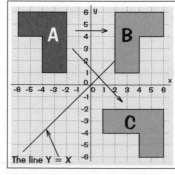

The line Y = X

With reflection, the POSITION and ORIENTATION of the object are the only things that change.

The Four Transformations

Combinations of Transformations

The examiners might make you do two transformations to the same shape, then ask you to describe the single transformation that would get you to the final shape. It's not as bad as it looks...

EXAMPLE 1: a) Reflect shape A in the x-axis. Label this shape B.
   b) Reflect shape B in the y-axis. Label this shape C.
   c) Describe the single transformation that will map shape A onto shape C.

ANSWER:

For a) and b), just draw the reflections.

For c), you can ignore shape B and just work out how to get from A to C. You can see it's a rotation, but the tricky bit is working out the centre of rotation. Use tracing paper if you need to.

The transformation from A to C is a rotation of 180° clockwise (or anticlockwise) about the origin.

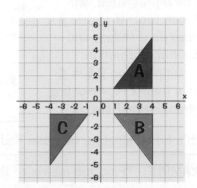

You might also be asked to spot what combination of two transformations takes one shape to another. Don't panic — you'll be fine as long as you've LEARNT the four transformations really well.

EXAMPLE 2: "What combination of two transformations takes you from triangle A to triangle B?"

METHOD: TRY AN OBVIOUS TRANSFORMATION FIRST, AND SEE...

The answer can only be a combination of two of the four types, so you can immediately start to narrow it down:

1) Since the shapes are the same size and shape we can rule out enlargements.

2) Next, try a reflection (in either the x-axis or the y-axis). Here we've tried a reflection in the y-axis, to give shape A':

3) You should now easily be able to see the final step from A' to B — it's a translation of $\binom{0}{6}$.

And that's it DONE — from A to B is simply a combination of:

A REFLECTION IN THE Y-AXIS followed by a TRANSLATION OF $\binom{0}{6}$

That's one answer anyway. If instead we decided to reflect in the x-axis first, we'd get another answer (see question 2 below) — but both are right.

It might not always be easy to see which transformation to try first. But the more transformation questions you do, the more obvious that first guess becomes.

Moving eet to ze left — a perfect translation...

Learn the transformations and the details that go with each. Then answer these:

1) Describe these transformations fully, in words: A → B, B → C, C → A, A → D.
2) In example 2 above, find the other transformation needed to get to shape B after reflecting shape A in the x-axis.

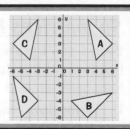

Extended

Matrix Transformations

So, time to put together everything from the last four pages into one swirling mass of numbers and shapes...

Matrices can Represent Shapes or Transformations

You can use a <u>matrix</u> to represent <u>any shape</u> on a coordinate grid.
Each <u>column</u> of the matrix is the <u>position vector</u> of <u>one corner</u> of the shape.

Some <u>transformations</u> can be represented with matrices too. If matrix <u>A</u> represents a shape, and <u>B</u> is a transformation, the multiplication <u>BA</u> = <u>C</u> gives a matrix representing the transformed shape.

EXAMPLE: $\underline{R} = \begin{pmatrix} 0 & -1 \\ 1 & 0 \end{pmatrix}$ gives a 90° anticlockwise rotation about the origin.

In the diagram on the right, $\underline{A} = \begin{pmatrix} 2 & 2 & 4 & 4 \\ 1 & 5 & 5 & 1 \end{pmatrix}$.

So $\underline{RA} = \begin{pmatrix} 0 & -1 \\ 1 & 0 \end{pmatrix}\begin{pmatrix} 2 & 2 & 4 & 4 \\ 1 & 5 & 5 & 1 \end{pmatrix} = \begin{pmatrix} -1 & -5 & -5 & -1 \\ 2 & 2 & 4 & 4 \end{pmatrix} = \underline{A}'$.

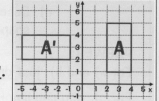

With a bit of <u>algebra</u>, you can find the matrix that represents a given transformation.

EXAMPLE: "Find the matrix of the transformation from <u>M</u> to <u>N</u>, as shown below."

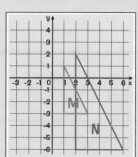

Call the transformation matrix $\underline{I} = \begin{pmatrix} a & b \\ c & d \end{pmatrix}$.

Then $\underline{TM} = \underline{N}$:

$$\overset{\text{T}}{\begin{pmatrix} a & b \\ c & d \end{pmatrix}}\overset{\text{M}}{\begin{pmatrix} 1 & 3 & 1 \\ 1 & -3 & -3 \end{pmatrix}} = \overset{\text{TM}}{\begin{pmatrix} a+b & 3a-3b & a-3b \\ c+d & 3c-3d & c-3d \end{pmatrix}} = \overset{\text{N}}{\begin{pmatrix} 2 & 6 & 2 \\ 2 & -6 & -6 \end{pmatrix}}$$

The entries in <u>TM</u> and <u>N</u> give you two sets of simultaneous equations (see p53):

$a + b = 2$, $3a - 3b = 6$, $a - 3b = 2$ $\rightarrow$ $a = 2$, $b = 0$ $\rightarrow$ $\underline{I} = \begin{pmatrix} 2 & 0 \\ 0 & 2 \end{pmatrix}$
$c + d = 2$, $3c - 3d = -6$, $c - 3d = -6$ $\rightarrow$ $c = 0$, $d = 2$

Combining Matrix Transformations

If a shape is transformed by <u>two matrices</u>, you have to multiply them in the <u>right order</u> — the matrix for the <u>transformation</u> you do <u>first</u> always goes <u>next to</u> the one for the <u>shape</u> you're transforming.

EXAMPLE: "Triangle $\underline{A} = \begin{pmatrix} 4 & 4 & 2 \\ 0 & 5 & 5 \end{pmatrix}$ is transformed by $\underline{R} = \begin{pmatrix} 0 & 1 \\ -1 & 0 \end{pmatrix}$ and then by $\underline{M} = \begin{pmatrix} -1 & 0 \\ 0 & 1 \end{pmatrix}$ to give triangle <u>B</u>. Find the matrix <u>B</u>."

The matrices have to be multiplied in the right order:
(second transformation) × (first transformation) × (original shape) = (new shape)

So we need $\underline{MRA} = \underline{B}$ — and it doesn't matter if you multiply $\underline{M} \times \underline{R}$ first, or $\underline{R} \times \underline{A}$:

$$\underline{M(RA)} = \overset{\text{M}}{\begin{pmatrix} -1 & 0 \\ 0 & 1 \end{pmatrix}}\overset{\text{R}}{\begin{pmatrix} 0 & 1 \\ -1 & 0 \end{pmatrix}}\overset{\text{A}}{\begin{pmatrix} 4 & 4 & 2 \\ 0 & 5 & 5 \end{pmatrix}} = \overset{\text{M}}{\begin{pmatrix} -1 & 0 \\ 0 & 1 \end{pmatrix}}\overset{\text{RA}}{\begin{pmatrix} 0 & 5 & 5 \\ -4 & -4 & -2 \end{pmatrix}} = \begin{pmatrix} 0 & -5 & -5 \\ -4 & -4 & -2 \end{pmatrix} = \underline{B}$$

OR

$$\underline{(MR)A} = \overset{\text{M}}{\begin{pmatrix} -1 & 0 \\ 0 & 1 \end{pmatrix}}\overset{\text{R}}{\begin{pmatrix} 0 & 1 \\ -1 & 0 \end{pmatrix}}\overset{\text{A}}{\begin{pmatrix} 4 & 4 & 2 \\ 0 & 5 & 5 \end{pmatrix}} = \overset{\text{MR}}{\begin{pmatrix} 0 & -1 \\ -1 & 0 \end{pmatrix}}\overset{\text{A}}{\begin{pmatrix} 4 & 4 & 2 \\ 0 & 5 & 5 \end{pmatrix}} = \begin{pmatrix} 0 & -5 & -5 \\ -4 & -4 & -2 \end{pmatrix} = \underline{B}$$

It's usually easier to multiply the transformation matrices together first.

So matrices have their uses after all... sort of...

Even I can't pretend this stuff isn't as grim as a grim thing. The best way to get your head round it is to do lots of questions. If the graph on the right looks familiar, it's because I stole it from the previous page. Shhh! Don't tell anyone...

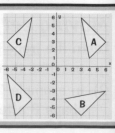

1) Write down the matrices representing these transformations: A → C, B → A.

Geometry

If you know <u>all</u> these rules <u>thoroughly</u>, you at least have a fighting chance of working out problems with lines and angles. If you don't — you've no chance. Sorry to break it to you like that.

7 Simple Rules — that's all:

I've not counted wrong — number 7 is on the next page.

1) Angles in a triangle

...ADD UP TO <u>180°</u>.

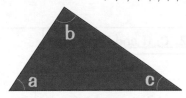

$$a+b+c=180°$$

2) Angles on a straight line

...ADD UP TO <u>180°</u>.

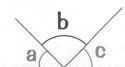

$$a+b+c=180°$$

3) Angles in a 4-sided shape (a 'Quadrilateral')

...ADD UP TO <u>360°</u>.

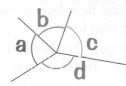

$$a+b+c+d=360°$$

4) Angles round a point

...ADD UP TO <u>360°</u>.

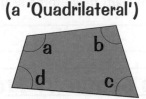

$$a+b+c+d=360°$$

5) Exterior Angle of Triangle

<u>EXTERIOR ANGLE</u> of triangle
= <u>SUM OF OPPOSITE INTERIOR ANGLES</u>

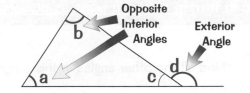

Opposite Interior Angles

Exterior Angle

$$a+b=d$$

6) Isosceles triangles

2 sides the same
2 angles the same

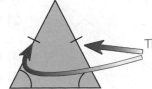

These dashes indicate two sides the same length

In an isosceles triangle, you only need to know <u>one angle</u> to be able to find the other two, which is very useful if you remember it.

a)

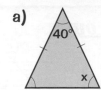

180° − 40° = 140°
<u>The two bottom angles are both the same</u> and they must add up to 140°, so each one must be half of 140°. So <u>x = 70°</u>.

b)

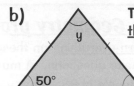

The <u>two bottom angles must be the same</u>, so 50° + 50° = 100°. All the angles add up to 180° so y = 180° − 100° = <u>80°</u>.

Geometry

7) Parallel Lines

Whenever one line crosses two <u>parallel lines</u> then the two bunches of angles <u>are the same</u>, and <u>a + b = 180°</u>.

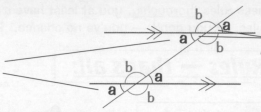

...and whenever two lines cross, the angles on opposite sides of the point where the lines meet are equal. Angles like these are called vertically opposite angles.

You need to spot the <u>characteristic Z, C, U and F shapes</u>:

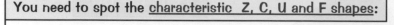

SAME

In a **Z-shape** they're called <u>'ALTERNATE ANGLES'</u>

ADD UP TO 180°

Any angles that add up to 180° are called <u>'SUPPLEMENTARY ANGLES'</u>

ADD UP TO 180°

In an **F-shape** they're called <u>'CORRESPONDING ANGLES'</u>

Alas you're expected to learn these three silly names too...

If necessary, **EXTEND THE LINES** to make the diagram <u>easier to get to grips with</u>:

The Basic Approach to Geometry Problems

1) <u>Don't</u> concentrate too much on the angle you have been asked to find. The best method is to find <u>ALL</u> the angles in <u>whatever order</u> they become obvious.

2) <u>Don't</u> sit there waiting for inspiration to hit you. It's all too easy to find yourself staring at a geometry problem and <u>getting nowhere</u>. The method is this:

> <u>GO THROUGH ALL THE ABOVE RULES OF GEOMETRY, ONE BY ONE</u>, and apply each of them in turn <u>in as many ways as possible</u> — one of them is bound to work.

Example

"Find all the other angles in this diagram."

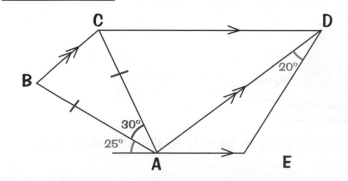

ANSWER:
1) ABC is isosceles, so ∠ABC = ∠ACB = 75°
2) BC and AD are parallel, BCAD is a Z-shape, so if ∠ACB = 75° then ∠CAD = 75° too.
3) Angles on a straight line means ∠EAD = 50°
4) AE and CD are parallel so ∠ADC = 50° also.
5) Triangle ACD adds up to 180° so ∠ACD = 55°
6) Triangle ADE adds up to 180° so ∠AED = 110°

The basic approach to Geometry problems — panic and freak out...

Well, you could. Or you could <u>learn everything</u> on these 2 pages, especially all the stuff on parallel lines, then have a go at these questions. A much better course of action methinks.

1) If one angle of an isosceles triangle is 68°, what values could the other angles have?
2) Find angle x in the diagram on the right and then fill in all the other angles.

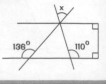

Circle Geometry

Bet you've always thought there's not much to know about circles. No corners, no angles... or so you thought. Well folks, grab your map and compass, as there's a whole lot more to discover. We're going in...

8 Simple Rules — That's all:

1) Angle in a Semicircle = 90°

A triangle drawn from the <u>two ends of a diameter</u> will ALWAYS make an <u>angle of 90° where it hits</u> the edge of the circle, no matter where it hits.

2) Tangent-Radius Meet at 90°

A <u>TANGENT</u> is a line that just touches a single point on the edge of the circle. A tangent always makes an angle of <u>exactly 90°</u> with the <u>radius</u> it meets at this point.

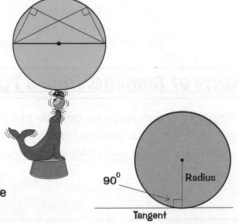
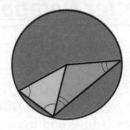

3) Sneaky Isosceles Triangles Formed by Two Radii

<u>Unlike other isosceles triangles</u> they <u>don't have the little tick marks on the sides</u> to remind you that they are the same — the fact that <u>they are both radii</u> is enough to make it an isosceles triangle.

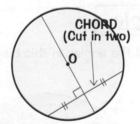

4) Chord Bisector is a Diameter

A <u>CHORD</u> is any line <u>drawn across a circle</u>. And no matter where you draw a chord, the line that <u>cuts it exactly in half</u> (at 90°), will <u>go through the centre of the circle</u> and so will be a <u>DIAMETER</u>.

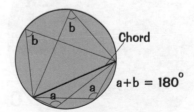

5) Angles in the Same Segment Are Equal

All triangles drawn from a chord will have <u>the same angle where they touch the circle</u>. Also, the two angles on opposite sides of the chord <u>add up to 180°</u>.

6) Angle at the Centre is Twice the Angle at the Edge

The angle subtended at the centre of a circle is <u>EXACTLY DOUBLE</u> the angle subtended at the edge of the circle from the same two points (two ends of the same chord). The phrase '<u>angle subtended at</u>' is nothing complicated, it's just a bit posher than saying '<u>angle made at</u>'.

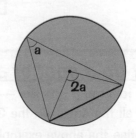

Circle Geometry

7) *Opposite Angles of a Cyclic Quadrilateral Add Up to 180°*

A <u>cyclic quadrilateral</u> is a <u>4-sided shape</u>
<u>with every corner touching</u> <u>the circle</u>.
Both pairs of opposite angles add up to 180°.

<u>a+c=180°</u>
<u>b+d=180°</u>

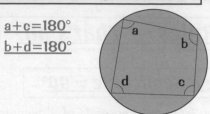

8) *Equality of Tangents from a Point*

The two tangents drawn from an outside point are
<u>always equal in length</u>, so creating an 'isosceles'
situation, with <u>two congruent right-angled triangles</u>.

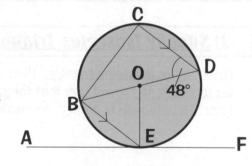

3-Letter Notation for Angles

1) <u>Angles are specified using 3 letters</u>, e.g. angle ODC = 48°

2) <u>THE MIDDLE LETTER IS WHERE THE ANGLE IS</u>

3) <u>THE OTHER TWO LETTERS</u> tell you <u>which lines enclose the angle</u>
For example: Angle ODC is <u>at D</u> and <u>enclosed by the lines</u> going
from <u>O to D</u> and from <u>D to C</u>.

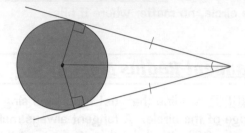

Example

"Find all the angles in this diagram."

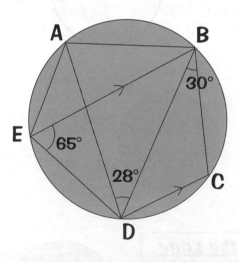

1) <u>PARALLEL LINES</u> — there are actually <u>4 different</u>
<u>lines</u> crossing the 2 parallel ones, but the most
useful one is ED which tells us that <u>EDC is 115°</u>

2) <u>ANGLE IN SAME SEGMENT</u> — there are potentially
<u>eight different chords</u> where this rule could apply,
but some are more useful than others:
EAD = EBD, ADB = AEB (so AEB = <u>28°</u>)
ABE = ADE, DAB = DEB (so DAB = <u>65°</u>)

3) <u>OPPOSITE ANGLES OF A CYCLIC QUADRILATERAL</u>
— looking at BEDC gives:
BCD = 180 – DEB = 180 – 65 = <u>115°</u>
— looking at ABDE gives:
ABD = 180 – AED = 180 – (28 + 65) = <u>87°</u>

4) <u>ANGLES IN A TRIANGLE ADD UP TO 180°</u> — this,
the simplest of all the rules, will now find all the
other angles for you.

Might do a spot of angling after lunch...

You can join me if you like — but you need to learn all about circles first. Oh, and correctly answer these:

1) Find all the angles in the 3rd diagram above illustrating the 3-letter notation (ODC = 48°, etc.).

2) <u>Practise the above example</u> till you <u>understand every step</u> and can do it easily without help.

Pythagoras' Theorem and Bearings

Pythagoras' theorem sounds hard but it's actually <u>dead simple</u>. It's also dead important, so make sure you really get your teeth into it. Once you've done that, there are some tasty bites on <u>bearings</u> to chew on too.

Pythagoras' Theorem — $a^2 + b^2 = h^2$

1) <u>PYTHAGORAS' THEOREM</u> always goes hand in hand with <u>sin</u>, <u>cos</u> and <u>tan</u> because they're both involved with <u>RIGHT-ANGLED TRIANGLES</u>.

2) The big difference is that Pythagoras does not involve any <u>angles</u> — it just uses <u>two sides</u> to find the <u>third side</u>. (sin, cos and tan always involve <u>ANGLES</u>.)

3) The <u>BASIC FORMULA</u> for Pythagoras is $\boxed{a^2 + b^2 = h^2}$

4) <u>PLUG THE NUMBERS IN</u> and work it out.

5) But get the numbers in the <u>RIGHT PLACE</u>. The 2 shorter sides (squared) add to equal the longest side (squared).

6) Always <u>CHECK</u> that your answer is <u>SENSIBLE</u>.

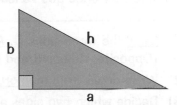

EXAMPLE:	
"Find the missing side in the triangle shown."	

5 m   3 m

<u>ANSWER</u>: $a^2 + b^2 = h^2$
$\therefore 3^2 + x^2 = 5^2$
$\therefore 9 + x^2 = 25$
$\therefore x^2 = 25 - 9 = 16$
$\therefore x = \sqrt{16} = \underline{4\ m}$

(Is it <u>sensible</u>? — Yes, it's shorter than 5 m, but not too much shorter.)

Bearings

To find or plot a bearing you must remember <u>the three key words</u>:

1) 'FROM'	<u>Find the word 'FROM' in the question</u>, and put your pencil on the diagram at the point you are going '<u>from</u>'.

2) NORTHLINE	At the point you are going <u>FROM</u>, <u>draw in a NORTHLINE</u>

3) CLOCKWISE	Now draw in the angle CLOCKWISE <u>from the northline to the line joining the two points</u>. This angle is the required bearing.

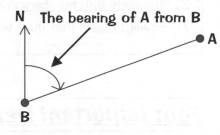

N   The bearing of A from B

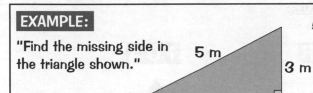

EXAMPLE:	"Find the bearing of Q <u>from P</u>":

1) 'From P'

2) <u>Northline</u> at P

3) <u>Clockwise</u>, from the N-line. This angle is the <u>bearing of Q from P</u> and is <u>245°</u>.

N.B. <u>All bearings should be given as 3 figures</u>, e.g. 176°, 034° (not 34°), 005° (not 5°), 018° etc.

Please bear with me while I figure out where we are...

Learn the <u>6 facts about Pythagoras</u> and the <u>3 key words for bearings</u>. Then <u>turn over and scribble 'em down</u>.

1) Find the length of BC.
2) Find the bearing of T from H, by measuring with a protractor.
3) <u>Calculate</u> the bearing of H from T.

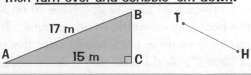

17 m   15 m

Trigonometry — Sin, Cos, Tan

Trigonometry — it's a big scary word. But it's not a big scary topic. An <u>important</u> topic, yes. An <u>always cropping up</u> topic, definitely. But scary? Pur-lease. Takes more than a triangle to scare me. Read on...

Method

There are several methods for doing Trig and they're all pretty much the same. However, the method shown below has a number of advantages, mainly because the <u>formula triangles</u> mean the <u>same method</u> is used <u>every time</u> (no matter which side or angle is being asked for). This makes the whole topic a lot simpler, and you'll find that once you've learned this method, the answers automatically come out right every time.

1) <u>Label</u> the three sides <u>O, A and H</u>
   (Opposite, Adjacent and Hypotenuse).

2) Write down <u>from memory</u> '<u>SOH CAH TOA</u>'.

3) Decide which <u>two sides</u> are <u>involved</u>: O,H A,H or
   O,A and select <u>SOH</u>, <u>CAH</u> or <u>TOA</u> accordingly.

4) Turn the one you choose into a <u>FORMULA TRIANGLE</u>:

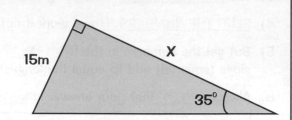

5) <u>Cover up</u> the thing you want to find (with your finger), and write down whatever is left showing.

6) <u>Translate into numbers</u> and work it out.

7) Finally, <u>check</u> that your answer is <u>sensible</u>.

Four Important Details

1) The <u>Hypotenuse</u> is the <u>LONGEST SIDE</u>. The <u>Opposite</u> is the side <u>OPPOSITE</u> the angle <u>being used</u> (θ), and the <u>Adjacent</u> is the (other) side <u>NEXT TO</u> the angle <u>being used</u>.

2) In the formula triangles, Sθ represents sin θ, Cθ is cos θ, and Tθ is tan θ.

3) Remember, <u>TO FIND THE ANGLE — USE INVERSE</u>. i.e. press ⁿᴵⁿⱽ or ˢᴴᴵᶠᵀ or ²ⁿᵈ, followed by <u>sin</u>, <u>cos</u> or <u>tan</u> (and make sure your calculator is in DEG mode).

4) You can only use sin, cos and tan on <u>RIGHT-ANGLED TRIANGLES</u> — you may have to add lines to the diagram to create one, especially with <u>isosceles triangles</u>.

Charlie made one final attempt to preserve the scary reputation of the triangles.

SOH CAH TOA — the not-so-secret formula for success...

See — not scary at all. All you have to do is <u>learn</u> this one simple method and you'll be SOH-CAH-TOAing along with the best trigonometric minds around. Notice the strategic use of the word "learn" though. It doesn't say "All you have to do is skim briefly over this method and you'll be a trig whizz". No my friend, it doesn't say that, it says "learn". And I shall say it once more for good measure — "learn" this method. And the job's a <u>good-un</u>.

Trigonometry — Sin, Cos, Tan

Thought you'd been left with no lovely examples to help you through the trials of trig? Not on your nelly...

Examples:

EXAMPLE 1:

"Find x in the triangle shown."

1) Label O, A, H

2) Write down 'SOH CAH TOA'

3) Two sides <u>involved</u>: O, H

4) So use

5) We want to find H so cover it up to leave: $H = \dfrac{O}{S\theta}$

6) Translate: $x = \dfrac{15}{\sin 35}$

Press ⬜15 ⬜÷ ⬜SIN ⬜35 ⬜=   `26.151702`

So ans = <u>26.2</u> m

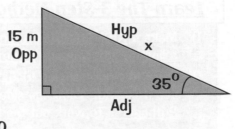

Check it's sensible: yes it's about twice as big as 15, as the diagram suggests.

EXAMPLE 2:

"Find the angle θ in this triangle."

1) Label O, A, H

2) Write down 'SOH CAH TOA'

3) Two sides <u>involved</u>: A, H

4) So use

5) We want to find θ so cover up Cθ to leave: $C\theta = \dfrac{A}{H}$

6) Translate: $\cos \theta = \dfrac{15}{25} = 0.6$

<u>NOW USE INVERSE:</u>   θ = INV cos (0.6)

Press ⬜INV ⬜COS ⬜0.6 ⬜=   `53.130102`

So ans. = <u>53.1°</u>

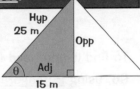

Note the usual way of dealing with an <u>ISOSCELES TRIANGLE</u>: split it <u>down the middle</u> to get a <u>RIGHT ANGLE</u>:

Finally, is it sensible? — Yes, the angle looks about 50°.

Angles of Elevation And Depression

A sad donkey. Poor donkey.

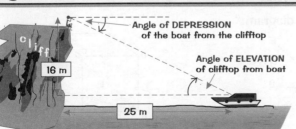

Angle of DEPRESSION of the boat from the clifftop

Angle of ELEVATION of clifftop from boat

1) The <u>Angle of Depression</u> is the angle <u>downwards</u> from the horizontal.

2) The <u>Angle of Elevation</u> is the angle <u>upwards</u> from the horizontal.

3) The Angles of Elevation and Depression are <u>EQUAL</u>.

The angle of depression — from your eyes to your revision...

Sadly for you, this depressing angle is one you need to be pretty familiar with. So adopt the position and...

1) Find x

2) Find θ

3) Calculate the angles of elevation and depression in the boat drawing above.

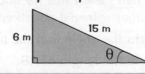

Extended

3D Pythagoras and Trigonometry

3D questions on Pythagoras and trig are a bit tricky. Or should that be a bit of a trick... for whilst they might <u>seem</u> fiendishly difficult, they're actually mild as a poor quality cheese. All you need is the same old rules.

Angle Between Line and Plane — Use a Diagram

Learn The 3-Step Method

1) Make a <u>RIGHT-ANGLED</u> triangle using <u>the line</u>, a line in the plane and <u>a line between the two</u>.

2) <u>Draw</u> this right-angled triangle again so that you can see it <u>clearly</u>. Label the sides. You might have to use <u>Pythagoras</u> to work out the length of one of the sides.

3) Use <u>trigonometry</u> to calculate the angle.

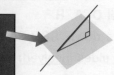

EXAMPLE:

"ABCDE is a square-based pyramid. It is 12 cm high and the square base has sides of length 7 cm. Find the angle the edge AE makes with the base."

> X is the centre of the square base.

1) First draw a <u>right-angled triangle</u> using the <u>edge AE</u>, the <u>base</u> and <u>a line between the two</u> (in this case the central height). Call the angle you're trying to find <u>θ</u>.

2) Now draw this triangle <u>clearly</u> and label it.

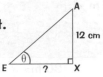

To find θ, you need to know the length of side **EX**.

So, using <u>Pythagoras</u> — $EX^2 = 3.5^2 + 3.5^2 = 24.5 \Rightarrow EX = \sqrt{24.5}$ cm

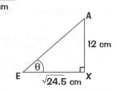

> You know the lengths of the <u>opposite</u> and <u>adjacent</u> sides, so use <u>tan</u>.

3) Now use <u>trigonometry</u> to find the angle θ:

$$\tan \theta = \frac{12}{\sqrt{24.5}} = 2.4... \quad \theta = \underline{67.6°} \text{ (1 d.p.)}$$

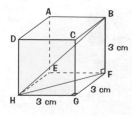

Use Right-Angled Triangles To Find Lengths too

EXAMPLE: "Find the lengths FH and BH shown in the diagram."

1) First use <u>Pythagoras</u> to find the length <u>FH</u>.

$FH^2 = 3^2 + 3^2 = 18 \Rightarrow FH = \sqrt{18}$ cm

2) Now use <u>Pythagoras</u> again to find the length <u>BH</u>.

$BH^2 = 3^2 + (\sqrt{18})^2 = 27 \Rightarrow BH = \sqrt{27}$ cm $= \underline{5.2 \text{ cm}}$ (1 decimal place)

Wow — just what can't right-angled triangles do?...

Well, they can't learn this for you. Or bake a cake. Or answer either of these rather splendid questions. You'll just have to do it yourself.

1) Calculate the angle that the line AG makes with the base of this cuboid.

2) Calculate the length of AG.

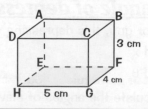

The Sine and Cosine Rules

Normal trigonometry using SOH CAH TOA etc. can only be applied to <u>right-angled</u> triangles. Which leaves us with the question of what to do with other-angled triangles. Step forward the <u>Sine and Cosine Rules</u>...

Labelling The Triangle

This is very important. You must label the sides and angles properly so that the letters for the sides and angles correspond with each other:

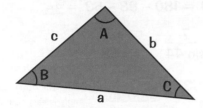

Remember, <u>side 'a' is opposite angle A</u> etc.

It doesn't matter which sides you decide to call a, b, and c, just as long as the angles are then labelled properly.

Three Formulas to Learn:

These first two formulas let you work out <u>sides</u> and <u>angles</u>:

The Sine Rule

You don't use the whole thing with both '=' signs of course, so it's not half as bad as it looks — you just choose the two bits that you want:

$$\frac{a}{\sin A} = \frac{b}{\sin B} = \frac{c}{\sin C}$$

e.g. $\frac{b}{\sin B} = \frac{c}{\sin C}$ or $\frac{a}{\sin A} = \frac{b}{\sin B}$

The Cosine Rule

$$a^2 = b^2 + c^2 - 2bc \cos A$$

or $\cos A = \dfrac{b^2 + c^2 - a^2}{2bc}$

Area of the Triangle

Of course, you already know the simple formula when you have the <u>base</u> and <u>vertical height</u>:

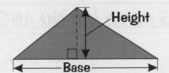

Area = ½ base × height

Well, here's a fancier formula that you can use when you know <u>two sides</u> and the angle <u>between them</u>:

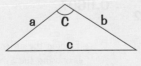

<u>Area of triangle = ½ ab sin C</u>

You need to <u>LEARN</u> all of these formulas off by heart and practise using them. If you don't, you won't be able to use them in the Exam, even if they give them to you.

...and step back again. Hope you enjoyed your moment in the spotlight...

With these extra rules, you will be able to conquer any triangles you come across. The next step is surely world domination — but only if you've learnt the formulas on this page and know how to properly label a triangle.

The Sine and Cosine Rules

Amazingly, there are only __FOUR__ question types where the _Sine_ and _Cosine_ rules would be applied. Learn the exact details of these four examples and you'll be laughing. WARNING: if you laugh too much people will think you're crazy.

The Four Examples

Extended

TWO ANGLES given plus ANY SIDE — SINE RULE NEEDED

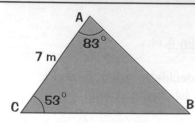

1) Don't forget the obvious: $B = 180 - 83 - 53 = \underline{44^\circ}$

2) Then use $\dfrac{b}{\sin B} = \dfrac{c}{\sin C} \Rightarrow \dfrac{7}{\sin 44} = \dfrac{c}{\sin 53}$

3) Which gives $\Rightarrow c = \dfrac{7 \times \sin 53}{\sin 44} = \underline{8.05 \text{ m}}$

Finding the other side and angle is easy using the SINE RULE

TWO SIDES given plus an ANGLE NOT ENCLOSED by them — SINE RULE NEEDED

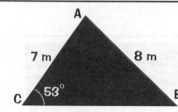

1) Use: $\dfrac{b}{\sin B} = \dfrac{c}{\sin C} \Rightarrow \dfrac{7}{\sin B} = \dfrac{8}{\sin 53}$

2) $\Rightarrow \sin B = \dfrac{7 \times \sin 53}{8} = 0.6988 \Rightarrow B = \sin^{-1}(0.6988) = \underline{44.3^\circ}$

Finding the other angle and side is easy using the SINE RULE

Extended

TWO SIDES given plus THE ANGLE ENCLOSED by them — COSINE RULE NEEDED

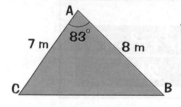

1) Use: $a^2 = b^2 + c^2 - 2bc \cos A$

$= 7^2 + 8^2 - 2 \times 7 \times 8 \times \cos 83$

$= 99.3506 \Rightarrow a = \sqrt{99.3506} = \underline{9.97 \text{ m}}$

Finding the other angles is easy using the SINE RULE

ALL THREE SIDES given but NO ANGLES — COSINE RULE NEEDED

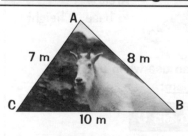

1) Use: $\cos A = \dfrac{b^2 + c^2 - a^2}{2bc}$

$= \dfrac{49 + 64 - 100}{2 \times 7 \times 8} = \dfrac{13}{112} = 0.11607$

2) Hence $A = \cos^{-1}(0.11607) = \underline{83.3^\circ}$

Finding the other angles is easy using the SINE RULE

Extended

Four examples + three formulas + two rules = one trigonometric genius...

And that genius'll be you. So get to it — learn the page, ace your Exam, live with success and joy. Aaah.

1) Write down __a new version__ of each of the 4 examples above and then use the SINE and COSINE RULES to find __ALL of the sides and angles__ for each one.

2) A triangle has two sides of 12 m and 17 m with an angle of 70° between them.
Find all the other sides and angles in the triangle. (A sketch is essential, of course).

Section Six — Angles and Geometry

Sine and Cosine for Larger Angles

The <u>sine</u> and <u>cosine</u> examples you've seen so far have all dealt with <u>acute angles</u>.
But you need to know about sin and cos of <u>obtuse angles</u>, too.

Graphs of Sin and Cos

1) You can find sin x and cos x for <u>any</u> value of x. The <u>full graphs</u> of sin x and cos x look like this:

2) So far all the examples in this book have used <u>acute</u> or <u>right angles</u>, but you also need to know about <u>obtuse angles</u>.

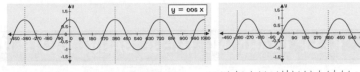
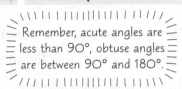

Remember, acute angles are less than 90°, obtuse angles are between 90° and 180°.

Cosine of Obtuse Angles

Values of cos x for obtuse angles are <u>negative</u>, but the cosine rule works just the same as for acute angles.

EXAMPLE: "Find the size of angle C."

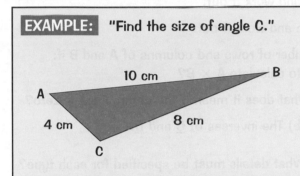

ANSWER:

1) One angle is obtuse, but the cosine rule still works:

$$\cos C = \frac{a^2 + b^2 - c^2}{2ab}$$
$$= \frac{64 + 16 - 100}{2 \times 4 \times 8} = \frac{-20}{64} = -0.3125$$

2) Hence $C = \cos^{-1}(-0.3125) = \underline{108.2°}$

Sine of Obtuse Angles

1) You have to be a bit more careful with sine. Each value of <u>sin x</u> between 0 and 1 corresponds to <u>2 different values</u> of x between 0° and 180°.

2) When you use your calculator's sin⁻¹ function to find the size of the angle, it gives you the answer between <u>0° and 90°</u>. If you know the angle is <u>obtuse</u>, you then have to <u>subtract</u> the answer you get from the calculator from <u>180°</u>.

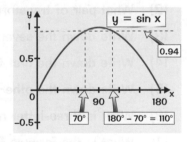

EXAMPLE: "Find the size of angle C."

ANSWER:

1) Use: $\frac{a}{\sin A} = \frac{c}{\sin C} \Rightarrow \frac{8}{\sin 49.5} = \frac{10}{\sin C}$

2) $\Rightarrow \sin C = \frac{10 \times \sin 49.5}{8} = 0.9505$

3) The calculator gives sin⁻¹(0.9505) = 71.9°. Looking at the triangle, this is obviously <u>too small</u> — the real angle C is <u>obtuse</u>. So C = 180° − 71.9° = <u>108.1°</u>

If you see an obtuse angle — don't ignore the warning sine...

...or should that be the sine warning... Make sure you remember that what comes out of your calculator for sin⁻¹ x isn't necessarily the size of your angle. Don't get caught out — always make sure your answer is sensible.

1) If 90° < x < 180°, find x when: a) sin x = 0.5,   b) sin x = 0.125,   c) sin x = 0.98
2) In a triangle ABC, the size of angle A is 40°, the length of side a is 5 cm and the length of side b is 7 cm. What are the two possible values of the size of angle B?

Revision Summary

Here we are again — more lovely questions for you to test yourself with.

Remember you have to keep practising these questions <u>over and over again</u> until you can answer them <u>all</u>. Seriously, you do. That's the best kind of revision there is because the whole idea is to find out what you <u>don't know</u> and then learn it <u>until you do</u>.   Enjoy.

KEEP LEARNING THESE BASIC FACTS UNTIL YOU KNOW THEM

1)   What are the four vector notations?

2)   What's the main rule for adding vectors?

3)   In a typical Exam question, what is the basic rule for finding an unknown vector?

4)   How do you find the magnitude of a vector?

5)   Produce your own 'swimming across the river' question and work it out.

6)   Produce your own 'swimming slightly upstream' question and work it out.

7)   <u>A</u> and <u>B</u> are matrices. What must be true about the number of rows and columns of A and B if:
     a) it's possible to calculate <u>A</u> + <u>B</u>   b) it's possible to calculate <u>A</u> × <u>B</u>?

8)   How do you find the determinant of a 2×2 matrix? What does it mean if the determinant is zero?

9)   If $\underline{C} = \begin{pmatrix} 2 & 5 \\ 1 & 2 \end{pmatrix}$ and $D = \begin{pmatrix} 0 & 3 \\ 6 & 8 \end{pmatrix}$, find: a) $\underline{C} \times \underline{D}$,   b) The inverses of $\underline{C}$ and $\underline{D}$.

10)   List all the types of transformation you need to know. What details must be specified for each type?

11)   What pair of transformations will convert shape C into shape D? ➡

12)   What pair of transformations will convert shape D to shape C?

13)   Write down the seven easy rules of geometry.

14)   Write down the first two simple rules for circle geometry.

15)   Write down the other seven rules for circle geometry.

16)   What is three-letter notation? Give an example.

17)   What is the formula for Pythagoras' theorem? What do you use Pythagoras for?

18)   Calculate the length of the hypotenuse of the triangle shown in the diagram. ➡

19)   What are the three key words for bearings? How must bearings be written?

20)   Write down the important steps of a good solid method for doing **TRIG**.

21)   Calculate the size of angle x shown in the diagram.

22)   Draw a diagram to illustrate angles of elevation and depression.

23)   What three steps allow you to find the angle between a line and a plane?

24)   Write down the **SINE** and **COSINE RULES** and draw a properly labelled triangle.

25)   List the 4 different types of sine/cosine rule questions and which rule you need for each.

26)   What is the formula (involving sin) for the area of any triangle? Demonstrate its use.

27)   What happens if you use the $\sin^{-1}$ function on your calculator to find the size of an obtuse angle?
      How do you use the result to find the actual size of the angle?

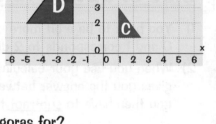

Mean, Median, Mode and Range

If you don't manage to learn these 4 basic definitions then you'll be passing up on some of the easiest marks in the whole Exam. It can't be that difficult can it?

> 1) <u>MODE</u> = <u>MOST</u> common
>
> 2) <u>MEDIAN</u> = <u>MIDDLE</u> value
>
> 3) <u>MEAN</u> = <u>TOTAL</u> of items ÷ <u>NUMBER</u> of items
>
> 4) <u>RANGE</u> = How far from the smallest to the biggest

The Golden Rule

Mean, median and mode should be <u>easy marks</u> but even people who've gone to the incredible extent of learning them still manage to lose marks in the Exam because they don't do <u>this one vital step</u>:

Always REARRANGE the data in ASCENDING ORDER

(and check you have the same number of entries!)

Example

"Find the mean, median, mode and range of these numbers:"
2, 5, 3, 2, 6, -4, 0, 9, -3, 1, 6, 3, -2, 3   (14)

1) FIRST... rearrange them: -4, -3, -2, 0, 1, 2, 2, 3, 3, 3, 5, 6, 6, 9 (14)✓

2) MEAN = $\dfrac{\text{total}}{\text{number}}$ = $\dfrac{-4-3-2+0+1+2+2+3+3+3+5+6+6+9}{14}$

= 31 ÷ 14 = <u>2.21</u>

3) MEDIAN = <u>the middle value</u> (only when they are <u>arranged in order of size</u>, that is!).

When there are two middle numbers as in this case, then the median is **HALFWAY BETWEEN THE TWO MIDDLE NUMBERS**.

> -4, -3, -2, 0, 1, 2, 2, 3, 3, 3, 5, 6, 6, 9
> ← seven numbers this side ⬆ seven numbers this side →
>
> Median = <u>2.5</u>

4) MODE = <u>most</u> common value, which is simply <u>3</u>. (Or you can say, "The <u>modal</u> value is 3.")

5) RANGE = distance from lowest to highest value, i.e. from -4 up to 9 = <u>13</u>

> The mean tends to be most useful, since it uses all the data in its calculation.

Choose the Most Appropriate Average

THE MEAN: The mean's often used to compare <u>performances</u> of people or items, such as cricketers' batting averages, golfers' handicaps or the lifetimes of batteries.

THE MEDIAN: This is a good average to use if you have some <u>extreme values</u>.

THE MODE: It's mainly used with <u>discrete</u> data, as continuous data might not have two values the same.

> DISCRETE DATA can only take specific values. E.g. the number of pupils in a school, favourite lesson.

One <u>advantage</u> the mode has over the mean and median is that it can be used in <u>qualitative data</u>. E.g. Which school subject is the most popular? What flavour ice cream sells the most?

> CONTINUOUS DATA can take any value in a certain range. E.g. height, weight, time.

Strike a pose, there's nothing to it — mode...

REMEMBER — <u>mode</u> = <u>most</u> (emphasise the 'o' in each when you say them); <u>median</u> = <u>mid</u> (emphasise the m*d in each when you say them); <u>mean</u> is just the <u>average</u>, but it's <u>mean</u> 'cos you have to work it out.
Learn the <u>four definitions</u> and the <u>golden rule</u>... then turn this page over and write them down from memory.
Then apply all that you have <u>learnt</u> to this set of data: 1, 3, 14, -5, 6, -12, 18, 7, 23, 10, -5, -14, 0, 25, 8.

Sampling Methods

Before you can start handling data, you have to collect it — there are different ways you can go about this...

You Always Want to Find Out About a Population

1) There are two types of data:

PRIMARY DATA is <u>data</u> you have collected <u>yourself</u>. — e.g. through a <u>survey</u> or an <u>experiment</u>.

SECONDARY DATA is data <u>someone else</u> has collected. — e.g. from <u>newspapers</u>, the <u>internet</u>, <u>databases</u> and <u>historical records</u>.

2) Whichever type of data you're using, you need to be clear about what your <u>population</u> is. The population is the group you want to know about. E.g. All the pupils in a school, all the trees in a park.

3) You can collect data about <u>every member</u> of the population, but this is usually impossible (or just too time-consuming or expensive). So you often have to take a <u>sample</u>, which means you somehow have to select a limited number of individuals so that they <u>properly represent the whole 'population'</u>.

Learn these Four Types of Sampling

<u>RANDOM</u> — this is where you just select individuals 'at random'. In practice it can be surprisingly difficult to make the selection truly random.

<u>SYSTEMATIC</u> — Start with a random selection and select every 10th or 100th one after that.

<u>STRATIFIED</u> — the population is divided into "strata" or "layers" — groups that don't overlap, like age ranges or sexes. Individuals are then randomly selected from each strata. How many you select from a strata is proportional to how many there are in that strata.

<u>QUOTA</u> — this is like stratified sampling in that you know how many individuals from each group are needed to represent the population, e.g. 10 girls and 10 boys. The difference is, you don't select them randomly — you just use the first ones you come across.

Spotting Problems With Sampling Methods

In practice, the most important thing you should be able to do is spot problems with sampling techniques, which means look for ways that the sample might <u>not be a true reflection of the population</u>. One mildly amusing way to practise, is to think up examples of bad sampling techniques:

1) A survey of motorists carried out in London concluded that 85% of British people drive Black Cabs.

2) Two surveys carried out on the same street corner asked, "Do you believe in God?" One found 90% of people didn't and the other found 90% of people did. The reason for the discrepancy? — one was carried out at 11pm Saturday night and the other at 10.15am Sunday morning.

3) A telephone survey carried out in the evening asked, "What do you usually do after work or school?". It found that 80% of the population usually stay in and watch TV. A street survey conducted at the same time found that only 30% usually stay in and watch TV. Astonishing.

I thought a sampling was a baby tree diagram...

Learn the names of the <u>four sampling techniques</u> with their brief descriptions, and the <u>problems</u> above. Time for...

1) A survey was done to investigate the average age of cars on Britain's roads by standing on a motorway bridge and noting the registration of the first 200 cars. Give three reasons why this is a poor sampling technique and suggest a better approach.

Frequency Tables

Frequency tables are a way to organise your data to make it easier to analyse. You can either do them in rows or in columns of numbers. They can be quite confusing, but not if you learn these seven key points:

Seven Key Points

1) The word **FREQUENCY** just means **HOW MANY**, so a frequency table is nothing more than a 'How many in each group' table.

2) The **FIRST ROW** (or column) just gives the **GROUP LABELS**.

3) The **SECOND ROW** (or column) gives the **ACTUAL DATA**.

4) You have to **WORK OUT A THIRD ROW** (or column) yourself.

5) The **MEAN** is always found using: | 3rd Row Total ÷ 2nd Row Total |

6) The **MEDIAN** is found from the **MIDDLE VALUE** in the 2nd row.

7) The **RANGE** is found from the extremes of the first row.

Example

Here is a typical frequency table shown in both **ROW FORM** and **COLUMN FORM**:

No. of Sisters	Frequency
0	7
1	15
2	12
3	8
4	3
5	1
6	0

No. of Sisters	0	1	2	3	4	5	6
Frequency	7	15	12	8	3	1	0

Column Form

Row Form

There's no real difference between these two forms and you could get either one in your Exam. Whichever you get, make sure you remember these **THREE IMPORTANT FACTS**:

1) **THE 1ST ROW** (or column) gives us the **GROUP LABELS** for the different categories : i.e. 'no sisters', 'one sister', 'two sisters', etc.

2) **THE 2ND ROW** (or column) is the **ACTUAL DATA** and tells us **HOW MANY (people) THERE ARE** in each category i.e. 7 people had 'no sisters', 15 people had 'one sister', etc.

3) **BUT YOU SHOULD SEE THE TABLE AS UNFINISHED** because it still needs **A THIRD ROW** (or column) and **TOTALS** for the 2nd and 3rd rows, as shown on the next page:

Frequency Tables

And here they are — the <u>completed tables</u> you've been eagerly awaiting...

This is what the two types of table look like when they're completed:

No. of Sisters	0	1	2	3	4	5	6	Totals	
Frequency	7	15	12	8	3	1	0	46	(People asked)
No. × Frequency	0	15	24	24	12	5	0	80	(Sisters)

No. of Sisters	Frequency	No. × Frequency
0	7	0
1	15	15
2	12	24
3	8	24
4	3	12
5	1	5
6	0	0
Totals	46	80

(People asked)   (Sisters)

"WHERE DOES THE THIRD ROW COME FROM?"

....I hear you cry!

<u>THE THIRD ROW</u> (or column) is <u>ALWAYS</u> obtained by <u>MULTIPLYING</u> the numbers from the <u>FIRST 2 ROWS</u> (or columns).

THIRD ROW = 1ST ROW × 2ND ROW

Once the table is complete, you can easily find the <u>MEAN, MEDIAN, MODE AND RANGE</u> (see p.97) which is what they usually demand in the Exam:

Mean, Median, Mode and Range:

This is easy enough <u>if you learn it</u>. If you don't, you'll drown in a sea of numbers.

MEAN $= \dfrac{\text{3rd Row Total}}{\text{2nd Row Total}} = \dfrac{80}{46} = 1.74$ (sisters per person)

Mean sisters

MEDIAN — imagine the original data <u>SET OUT IN ASCENDING ORDER</u>:

0000000 111111111111111 222222222222 33333333 444 5
↑

and the median is just the middle number which is between the 23rd and 24th digits.

So for this data <u>THE MEDIAN IS 2</u>. (Of course, when you get slick at this you can easily find the position of the middle value straight from the table)

The MODE is very easy — it's just <u>THE GROUP WITH THE MOST ENTRIES</u>: i.e <u>1</u>

The RANGE is 5 – 0 = <u>5</u>   The 2nd row tells us there are people with anything from 'no sisters' right up to 'five sisters' (but not 6 sisters). (Always give it as a <u>single number</u>.)

What's this? No gag? Yes well I thought you might appreciate being able to reach the end of one page without having to endure a pathetic attempt at humour. See, I really do care. Normal service will be resumed on p101. Now learn the <u>7 rules</u> for frequency tables, then turn over and write them down to see what you know.

Using the methods you have just learned and this frequency table, find the MEAN, MEDIAN, MODE and RANGE of the no. of phones that people have.

No. of phones	0	1	2	3	4	5	6
Frequency	1	25	53	34	22	5	1

Grouped Frequency Tables

You often use GROUPED FREQUENCY TABLES when you've got a large range of data values — which would make a normal frequency table with too many rows. The data is split into groups using class intervals.

The table below shows the distribution of weights of 60 school kids:

Weight (kg)	$30 \leq w < 40$	$40 \leq w < 50$	$50 \leq w < 60$	$60 \leq w < 70$	$70 \leq w < 80$
Frequency	8	16	18	12	6

What does $30 \leq w < 40$ mean?

Don't get confused by the notation used for the class intervals.

1) the $\leq$ symbol means w can be greater than or equal to 30

2) the $<$ symbol means w must be less than 40 (but not equal to it)

So a value of 30 will go in this group, but a value of 40 will have to go in the next group up: $40 \leq w < 50$.

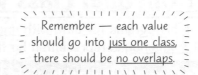

Remember — each value should go into just one class, there should be no overlaps.

'Estimating' The Mean using Mid-Interval Values

Just like with ordinary frequency tables you have to add extra rows and find totals to be able to work anything out. Also notice you can only 'ESTIMATE' the mean from grouped data tables — you can't find it exactly unless you know all the original values.

> 1) Add a 3rd row and enter MID-INTERVAL VALUES for each group.
>
> 2) Add a 4th row and multiply FREQUENCY × MID-INTERVAL VALUE for each group.

Weight (kg)	$30 \leq w < 40$	$40 \leq w < 50$	$50 \leq w < 60$	$60 \leq w < 70$	$70 \leq w < 80$	Totals
Frequency	8	16	18	12	6	60
Mid-Interval Value	35	45	55	65	75	—
Frequency × Mid-Interval Value	280	720	990	780	450	3220

1) ESTIMATING THE MEAN is then the usual thing of DIVIDING THE TOTALS:

$$\text{Mean} = \frac{\text{Overall Total (Last Row)}}{\text{Frequency Total (2nd Row)}} = \frac{3220}{60} = 53.7$$

2) THE MODE is still nice'n'easy: the modal group is $50 \leq w < 60$ kg.

3) THE MEDIAN can't be found exactly but you can say which group it's in. If all the data were put in order, the 30th/31st entries would be in the $50 \leq w < 60$ kg group.

Mid-interval value — cheap ice-creams...

Learn all the details on this page, then turn over and write down everything you've learned. Good clean fun.

1) Estimate the mean for this table:

2) Also state the modal group and the approximate value of the median.

Length L (cm)	$15.5 \leq L < 16.5$	$16.5 \leq L < 17.5$	$17.5 \leq L < 18.5$	$18.5 \leq L < 19.5$
Frequency	12	18	23	8

Extended

Histograms and Frequency Density

You'll be pleased to know that <u>histograms</u> are used to show frequency distributions for <u>continuous data</u>...

Histograms Can Have Equal Class Widths...

Histograms are similar to bar charts — they also show <u>frequency</u> using bars.
Drawing a histogram for data with equal class widths is easy... you put
<u>frequency</u> on the <u>y-axis</u> and a <u>suitable scale</u> for your data on the <u>x-axis</u>
— then you draw a <u>bar</u> for each <u>class</u>. But remember, in histograms there
are <u>no gaps</u> between the bars and the <u>x-axis</u> is <u>continuous</u>.

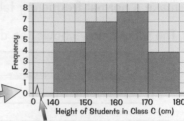

This squiggle is used to show that
some of the x-axis is missing.

...Or Unequal Class Widths

Drawing histograms for data with <u>unequal</u> class widths is trickier. The key thing to remember
is that <u>frequency</u> is represented by the <u>AREA</u> of the bars instead of the <u>height</u>.

1) To work out the <u>heights</u> of the bars you need to calculate the <u>frequency density</u> for each data class:

$$\text{FREQUENCY DENSITY} = \text{FREQUENCY} \div \text{CLASS WIDTH}$$

2) Then, draw the axes with <u>frequency density</u> on the y-axis and the <u>variable values</u> on the x-axis.

3) Now draw <u>bars</u> for each class — the <u>height</u> is the <u>frequency density</u> and the <u>width</u> is the <u>class width</u>.

EXAMPLE: "Use the table below to <u>complete</u> the <u>histogram</u>."

Pulse rate (bpm)	$65 \le p < 75$	$75 \le p < 80$	$80 \le p < 85$	$85 \le p < 95$
Frequency	14	15	20	33
Frequency density	1.4	3		

1) First, work out the missing
<u>frequency densities</u>:

$20 \div 5$
$= \underline{4}$ units

$33 \div 10$
$= \underline{3.3}$ units

2) Then <u>draw</u> the <u>bars</u>.

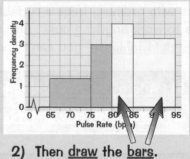

You can use Histograms to Estimate Frequencies

If you need to <u>estimate</u> the <u>frequency</u> for a given interval of values
you just need to <u>rearrange</u> the formula to get:
And then pop in the values from the <u>graph</u>.

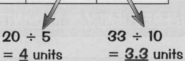

Frequency = Frequency Density × Class Width

EXAMPLE: "The histogram below shows the <u>heights</u> of <u>sunflowers</u> entered into a local competition.
<u>Estimate</u> how many sunflowers were between <u>170 and 179 cm</u> tall."

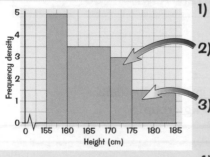

1) The <u>3rd</u> and <u>4th</u> bars cover the height range 170 – 179 cm — so you need
to break the calculation into <u>two chunks</u> and use the formula for each.

2) For the 3rd bar:
Class width = 175 – 170 = <u>5</u> and frequency density = <u>3</u>.
So, frequency = $\underline{5 \times 3 = 15}$.

3) For the 4th bar:
Class width remaining = 179 – 175 = <u>4</u> and frequency density = <u>1.5</u>.
So, frequency = $\underline{4 \times 1.5 = 6}$.

4) Add the frequencies together — 15 + 6 = <u>21 sunflowers</u>.

My brain frequently feels very dense...

Make sure you know that formula for frequency density off by heart. Then, you know the drill...
1) Using the histogram above, estimate the number of sunflowers between 155 and 162 cm tall.

Cumulative Frequency

Four Key Points

1) <u>CUMULATIVE FREQUENCY</u> just means <u>ADDING IT UP AS YOU GO ALONG</u>.

2) You have to <u>ADD A THIRD ROW</u> to the table — the <u>RUNNING TOTAL</u> of the 2nd row.

3) <u>When plotting the graph</u>, always plot points <u>using the HIGHEST VALUE in each group</u> (of row 1) with the value from <u>row 3</u>.   i.e. plot 13 at <u>160</u>, etc. (see below).

4) Cumulative Frequency is always plotted <u>up the side</u> of a graph, not across.

Example

Height (cm)	$140 \leq x < 150$	$150 \leq x < 160$	$160 \leq x < 170$	$170 \leq x < 180$	$180 \leq x < 190$	$190 \leq x < 200$	$200 \leq x < 210$
Frequency	4	9	20	33	36	15	3
Cumulative frequency	4 (at 150)	13 (at 160)	33 (at 170)	66 (at 180)	102 (at 190)	117 (at 200)	120 (at 210)

The graph is plotted from these pairs: (150, 4) (160, 13) (170, 33) (180, 66) etc.

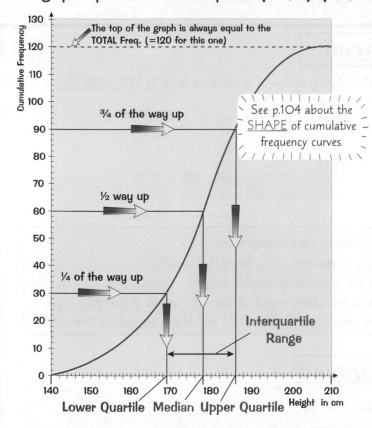

See p.104 about the <u>SHAPE</u> of cumulative frequency curves.

For a cumulative frequency curve there are <u>THREE VITAL STATISTICS</u> which you need to know how to find:

1) **MEDIAN**
<u>Exactly halfway UP</u>, then across, then down and <u>read off the bottom scale</u>.

2) **LOWER AND UPPER QUARTILES**
<u>Exactly ¼ and ¾ UP the side</u>, then across, then down and read off the <u>bottom scale</u>.

3) **INTERQUARTILE RANGE**
The distance <u>on the bottom scale</u> between the lower and upper quartiles.

So from the cumulative frequency curve for this data, we get these results:

MEDIAN = <u>178</u> cm
LOWER QUARTILE = <u>169</u> cm
UPPER QUARTILE = <u>186</u> cm
INTERQUARTILE RANGE = <u>17</u> cm   (186-169)

Percentiles Divide the Data into 100 Groups

1) You can use more groups to give a more flexible view of the spread of data. <u>PERCENTILES</u>, P_1 to P_{99}, divide the data into <u>one hundred</u> equal groups.

2) The P_{90} to P_{10} percentile range gives a more realistic idea of the spread of data than the range does. It gives the range of the middle 80% of the data, so ignores any outliers.

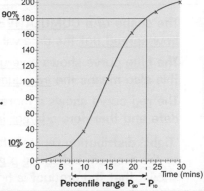

Percentile range $P_{90} - P_{10}$

Learn the whole range — interquartile, percentile and bog-standard...

Learn this page, then cover it up and do these:
Complete this cumulative frequency table. Draw the graph.
Find the 3 Vital Statistics. Then find the tenth percentile (P_{10}).

No of fish	41 – 45	46 – 50	51 – 55	56 – 60	61 – 65	66 – 70	71 – 75
Frequency	2	7	17	25	19	8	2

Spread of Data

Spread these pages out in front of you and get learning the different type of <u>graphs and charts</u>...

Scatter Graphs — Correlation and the Line of Best Fit

A scatter graph tells you how closely two things are related — the fancy word for this is <u>CORRELATION</u>. <u>Good correlation</u> means the two things are <u>closely related</u> to each other. <u>Poor correlation</u> means there is <u>very little relationship</u>. The <u>LINE OF BEST FIT</u> goes roughly <u>through the middle of the scatter of points</u>. (It doesn't have to go through any of the points exactly but it can.) If the line slopes <u>up</u> it's <u>positive correlation</u>, if it slopes <u>down</u> it's <u>negative correlation</u>. <u>No correlation</u> means there's no <u>linear relationship</u>.

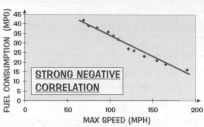

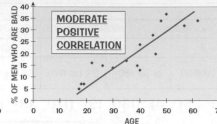

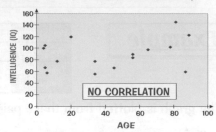

Shapes of Histograms and 'Spread'

You can easily estimate the mean from the shape of a histogram — it's more or less <u>IN THE MIDDLE</u>.

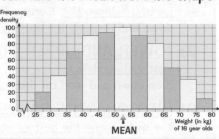

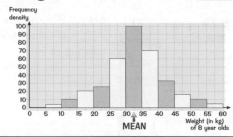

You must <u>LEARN the significance of the shapes</u> of these two histograms:

1) The first shows <u>high dispersion</u> (a <u>large spread</u> of results away from the mean). (i.e. the weights of a sample of 16 year olds will cover a very wide range)

2) The second shows a '<u>tighter</u>' distribution of results where most values are within a <u>narrow range</u> either side of the mean. (i.e the weights of a sample of 8 year olds will show <u>very little</u> variation)

Cumulative Freq. Curves and 'Spread'

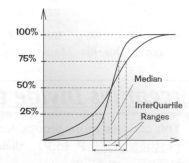

The shape of a <u>CUMULATIVE FREQUENCY CURVE</u> also tells us <u>how spread out</u> the data values are.

The <u>blue</u> curve shows a <u>very tight distribution</u> around the <u>MEDIAN</u> and this also means the <u>interquartile range is small</u> as shown.

The <u>red</u> curve shows a more <u>widely spread</u> set of data and therefore a <u>larger interquartile range</u>.

'Tight' distribution represents <u>CONSISTENT</u> results. E.g. the <u>lifetimes of light bulbs</u> would all be very close to the median, indicating a <u>good product</u>. The lifetimes of another product may show <u>wide variation</u>, which shows that the product is not as consistent. They often ask about this 'shape significance' in <u>Exams</u>.

Data spread — delicious and low in fat...

A nice 'n busy page this one — learn it all, turn over and write down all the <u>important details</u> from memory. Then:
1) Draw two contrasting histograms showing speeds of cyclists and motorists.
2) Sketch two cumulative frequency curves for heights of 5 yr olds and 13 yr olds.

Extended

Extended

Other Graphs and Charts

Ooo, now it's time for a graph where you get to draw <u>pretty pictures</u>. And some other types, but they're not as much fun. You've still got to know them though.

1) Pictograms — these use <u>pictures</u> instead of <u>numbers</u>.

In a <u>PICTOGRAM</u> each picture or symbol represents a certain number of items.

<u>EXAMPLE</u>: The <u>pictogram</u> opposite shows the number of talking cats used in ridiculous TV adverts in a 3-month period:

 = 500 talking cats

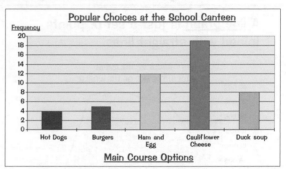

May		(1500 ridiculous talking cats)
June		(1250 ridiculous talking cats)
July		(2000 ridiculous talking cats)

2) Bar Charts — Just watch out for when the bars should touch or not touch:

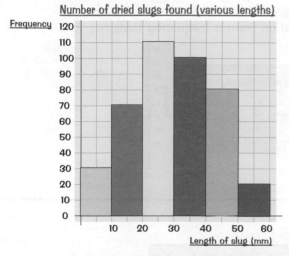

Number of dried slugs found (various lengths)

Length of slug (mm)

See page 97 for discrete and continuous data.

This bar chart compares <u>totally separate items</u> so the bars are <u>separate</u>. The data is <u>DISCRETE</u>.

Popular Choices at the School Canteen

Main Course Options

Bars showing <u>CONTINUOUS DATA</u> should <u>touch</u>. The bars in the chart above are for <u>LENGTHS</u> and you must <u>put every possible length into one bar or the next</u> so there mustn't be any spaces.

A <u>BAR-LINE GRAPH</u> is just like a bar chart except you draw thin lines instead of bars.

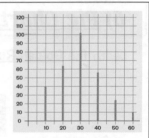

3) Stem and Leaf Diagrams

<u>Stem and leaf</u> diagrams are a bit like bar charts, but more confusing. They're supposed to be easy to read, but they're not. So <u>LEARN</u> this example.

EXAMPLE: This diagram shows the ages of my school teachers.
a) How many of the teachers are in their forties?
b) How old is the oldest teacher?
c) What is the median age?

ANSWER:

Step 1:
Write down all the ages of the teachers, using the key.

Step 2:
Answer the question.

33, 35,
40, 45, 47, (48),
51, 54, 59,
61, (63)

a) <u>four</u>
b) <u>63</u>
c) <u>48</u>

See p. 97 for how to find the median.

3	3 5
4	0 5 7 8
5	1 4 9
6	1 3

Key: 5 | 4 means 54

The key tells you how to read the diagram. A 5 in the stem and a 4 in the leaf means 54.

Other Graphs and Charts

4) Two-Way Tables

Two-way <u>tables</u> are a bit like frequency tables, but they show <u>two</u> things instead of just <u>one</u>.

EXAMPLE: "Use this table to work out how many
a) <u>right-handed people</u> and
b) <u>left-handed women</u> there were in this survey."

	Women	Men	TOTAL
Left-handed		27	63
Right-handed	164	173	
TOTAL	200	200	400

ANSWER:

a) 164 + 173 = <u>337 right-handed people</u> (or you could have done 400 – 63 = 337).

b) 200 – 164 = <u>36 left-handed women</u> (or you could have done 63 – 27 = 36). Easy.

5) Line Graphs and Frequency Polygons

A <u>line graph</u> is just a set of points joined with straight lines.

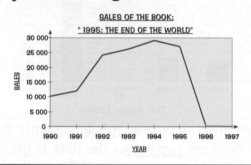

A <u>frequency polygon</u> looks similar and is used to show the information from a frequency table:

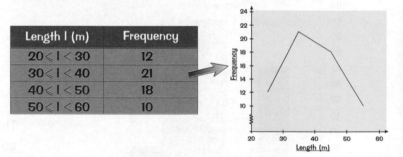

Length l (m)	Frequency
$20 \leqslant l < 30$	12
$30 \leqslant l < 40$	21
$40 \leqslant l < 50$	18
$50 \leqslant l < 60$	10

6) Pie Charts

Learn the <u>Golden Rule</u> for Pie Charts: **The TOTAL of Everything = 360°**

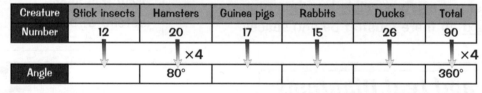

Creature	Stick insects	Hamsters	Guinea pigs	Rabbits	Ducks	Total
Number	12	20	17	15	26	90
Angle		80°				360°

×4 ... ×4

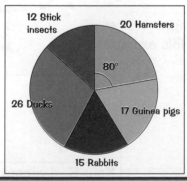

1) Add up all the numbers in each sector to get the <u>TOTAL</u> (90 for this one).

2) Then find the <u>MULTIPLIER</u> (or divider) that you need to <u>turn your total into 360°</u>: For 90 → 360 as above, the <u>MULTIPLIER</u> is 4.

3) Now <u>MULTIPLY EVERY NUMBER BY 4</u> to get the angle for each sector. E.g. the angle for hamsters will be 20 × 4 = <u>80°</u>.

I'm a multiplier, twisted multiplier...

Lotsa useful diagrams on the last two pages — learn all the details of the <u>six types of chart</u>. Got all that stored? Good...

1) Turn over the page and draw an example of each chart.

2) Work out the angles for all the other animals in the pie chart shown above.

Section Seven — Handling Data

Probability

Probability definitely seems a bit of a 'Black Art' to most people. It's not as bad as you think, but YOU MUST LEARN THE BASIC FACTS, which is what we have on these 3 pages.

All Probabilities are Between 0 and 1

Probabilities can only have values from 0 to 1 (including those values). You should be able to put the probability of any event happening on this scale of 0 to 1.

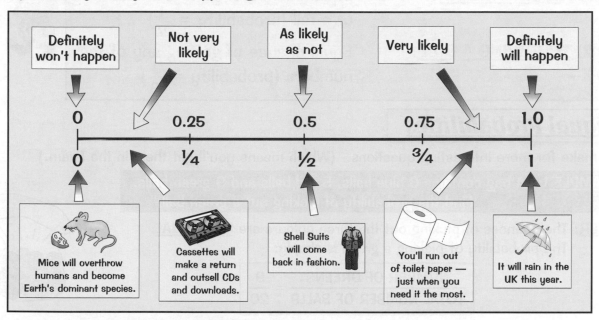

| Definitely won't happen | Not very likely | As likely as not | Very likely | Definitely will happen |

0   0.25   0.5   0.75   1.0

0   ¼   ½   ¾   1

Mice will overthrow humans and become Earth's dominant species.

Cassettes will make a return and outsell CDs and downloads.

Shell Suits will come back in fashion.

You'll run out of toilet paper — just when you need it the most.

It will rain in the UK this year.

Remember you can give probabilities using
FRACTIONS, DECIMALS or PERCENTAGES.

An Outcome is What Might Happen

1) An OUTCOME is something that can happen as a result of a TRIAL.
   (A trial can be anything from spinning a spinner to a horse race.)

2) For example, when you toss a coin, the only possible outcomes are heads and tails.

Use a Possibility Diagram to List all the Outcomes

A possibility diagram is a graph showing all the possible outcomes.

To draw one, use a grid with each line showing an outcome.
There's a different combination at each point where the lines cross.

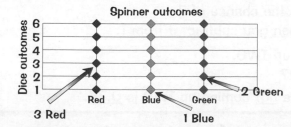

This diagram shows the possible outcomes when you throw a normal dice and spin a spinner with three colours.
It uses columns for the spinner outcomes and rows for the dice. It doesn't matter which way round you do it though.

A picture of cows colonising the moon — a vague possibility diagram...

This question should test if you've got the gist of possibility diagrams: Set up a diagram to list the possible outcomes of tossing a coin and randomly choosing one day next week to go shopping.

Section Seven — Handling Data

Probability

There's more to probability than just tossing coins and rolling dice you know. Oh yes.

Equal Probabilities

When the different results all have the same chance of happening, then the probabilities will be EQUAL. These are the two cases which usually come up in Exams:

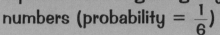

> 1) TOSSING A COIN: Equal chance of getting a head or a tail (probability = $\frac{1}{2}$)
>
> 2) THROWING A DICE: Equal chance of getting any of the numbers (probability = $\frac{1}{6}$)

I hope they don't ask me to toss this.

Unequal Probabilities

These make for more interesting questions. (Which means you'll get them in the Exam.)

> EXAMPLE 1: "A bag contains 6 blue balls, 5 red balls and 9 green balls. Find the probability of picking out a green ball."

ANSWER: The chances of picking out the three colours are NOT EQUAL. The probability of picking a green is simply:

$$\frac{\text{NUMBER OF GREENS}}{\text{TOTAL NUMBER OF BALLS}} = \frac{9}{20}$$

> EXAMPLE 2: "What is the probability of winning £45 on this spinner?"

ANSWER: The pointer has <u>the same chance</u> of stopping on <u>every sector</u>... ... and since there are 2 out of 8 which are £45 then it's a <u>2 out of 8 chance</u> of getting £45.

BUT REMEMBER ... you have to say this as a FRACTION or a DECIMAL or a PERCENTAGE:

> 2 out of 8 is 2 ÷ 8 which is <u>0.25</u> (as a decimal) or $\frac{1}{4}$ (as a fraction) or <u>25%</u> (as a percentage)

The Probability of Something Not Happening

The probability of the something <u>not happening</u> is just the rest of the probability that's <u>left over</u>. This is simple enough AS LONG AS YOU REMEMBER IT.

If the probability of something happening is, say, 0.3 then the chance of it NOT HAPPENING is 1 – 0.3 (= 0.7), i.e. it's what's left when you <u>subtract it from 1</u>.

Example: A loaded dice has a 0.25 chance of coming up TWO. What is the chance of it <u>not</u> coming up TWO?

Answer: 1 – 0.25 = 0.75. So, the chance of the dice <u>not</u> coming up TWO is <u>0.75</u>.

Spinners fashion tip #56 — gold hot pants are an absolute must......

Spinners and bags of balls come up a lot in the Exam. Don't panic if they use another example — you work it out in exactly the same way. Try this one: 1) What is the probability of picking a white puppy from a bag containing 3 black puppies, 4 brown puppies, 2 white puppies and one purple puppy?

Relative Frequency

This isn't the number of times your granny comes to visit. It's a way of working out <u>probabilities</u>. Since you asked, my granny visits twice a year. She says she'd like to visit more, but sleeping on the blow-up bed plays mischief with her bad back.

Fair or Biased?

The probability of rolling a five on a dice is $\frac{1}{6}$ — you know that each of the 6 numbers on a dice is <u>equally likely</u> to be rolled, and there's <u>only 1 five</u>.

BUT this only works if it's a <u>fair dice</u>. If the dice is a bit <u>wonky</u> (the technical term is 'biased') then each number <u>won't</u> have an equal chance of being rolled. That's where <u>Relative Frequency</u> comes in — you can use it to work out probabilities when things might be wonky.

Do the Experiment Again and Again and Again and Again

You need to do an experiment <u>over and over again</u> and then do a quick calculation. (Remember, an experiment could just mean rolling a dice.) Usually the results of these experiments will be written in a <u>table</u>.

The Formula for Relative Frequency

$$\text{Probability of something happening} = \frac{\text{Number of times it has happened}}{\text{Number of times you tried}}$$

You can work out the relative frequency as a <u>fraction</u> but usually <u>decimals</u> are best.

The important thing to remember is:

> The more times you do the experiment, the more accurate the probability will be.

Example:

Number of Times the dice was rolled	10	20	50	100
Number of threes rolled	2	5	11	23
Relative Frequency	$\frac{2}{10} = 0.2$	$\frac{5}{20} = 0.25$	$\frac{11}{50} = 0.22$	$\frac{23}{100} = 0.23$

So, what's the probability? We've got <u>4 possible answers</u>, but the best is the one worked out using the <u>highest number of dice rolls</u>. This makes the probability of rolling a three on this dice <u>0.23</u>.

And since for a fair, unbiased dice, the probability of rolling a three is $\frac{1}{6}$ (about 0.17), then our dice is probably <u>biased</u>.

Dice rolls — a crunchy pack lunch alternative...

Blast those wonky dice. That's what started all this. Still it's all bound to come up on the Exam. So...

1) A 3-sided spinner is spun 100 times — it lands on red 43 times, blue 24 times and green the other times. Calculate the relative frequency of each outcome.

Probability — Multiple Events

This is where most people start getting into trouble, and d'you know why?
I'll tell you — it's because they don't know the <u>three simple steps</u> and the <u>two rules</u> to apply:

Three Simple Steps

1) Always break down a complicated-looking probability question into <u>A SEQUENCE</u> of <u>SEPARATE SINGLE EVENTS</u>.
2) Find the probability of <u>EACH</u> of these <u>SEPARATE SINGLE EVENTS</u>.
3) Apply the <u>AND/OR</u> rule:

And now for the rules...

1) The AND Rule:

$$P(A \text{ and } B) = P(A) \times P(B)$$

Which means:
The probability of <u>Event A AND Event B BOTH</u> happening is equal to the two separate probabilities <u>MULTIPLIED together</u>.

(strictly speaking, the two events have to be <u>INDEPENDENT</u>. All that means is that one event happening does not in any way affect the other one happening. Contrast this with mutually exclusive below.)

2) The OR Rule:

$$P(A \text{ or } B) = P(A) + P(B)$$

Which means:
The probability of <u>EITHER Event A OR Event B happening</u> is equal to the two separate probabilities <u>ADDED together</u>.

(Strictly speaking, the two events have to be <u>MUTUALLY EXCLUSIVE</u> which means that if one event happens, the other one can't happen.)

The way to remember this is that it's the <u>wrong way round</u> — i.e. you'd want the AND to go with the + but it doesn't: It's '<u>AND with ×</u>' and '<u>OR with +</u>'.

Example

"Find the probability of picking two kings from a pack of cards (assuming you don't replace the first card picked)."

1) <u>SPLIT</u> this into <u>TWO SEPARATE EVENTS</u> — i.e. picking the <u>first king</u> and then <u>picking the second king</u>.

2) <u>Find the SEPARATE probabilities</u> of these two <u>separate events</u>:
$P(\text{1st king}) = \frac{4}{52}$ $P(\text{2nd king}) = \frac{3}{51}$ (— note the change from 52 to 51)

3) <u>Apply the AND/OR rule:</u>   <u>BOTH</u> events must happen, so it's the <u>AND</u> rule:
so <u>multiply</u> the two separate probabilities: $\frac{4}{52} \times \frac{3}{51} = \frac{1}{221}$

Revise — and/or eat cake...

Wowsers, lots of important stuff on this page. Learn the <u>three simple steps</u> for <u>multiple events</u>, and the <u>AND/OR rule</u> and you'll be fine and/or dandy in the Exam. Ahem. Now have a go at these little jokers below...

1) Find the probability of picking from a pack of cards (without replacement):
   a) 2 queens plus the ace of spades. b) A <u>pair</u> of Jacks, Queens or Kings

Probability — Tree Diagrams

Tree diagrams are all pretty much the same, so it's a pretty darned good idea to learn these basic details
(which apply to ALL tree diagrams) — ready for the one that's bound to be in the Exam.

General Tree Diagram

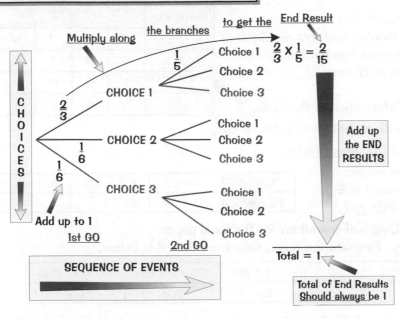

1) Always **MULTIPLY ALONG** the branches (as shown) to get the **END RESULTS**.
2) On any set of branches which all <u>meet at a point</u>, the numbers must always **ADD UP TO 1**.
3) <u>Check</u> that your diagram is correct by making sure the end results **ADD UP TO ONE**.
4) To answer any question, simply **ADD UP** the relevant **END RESULTS** (see below).

A Likely Tree Diagram Question

EXAMPLE: "A box contains 5 red disks and 3 green disks. Two disks are taken at random <u>without replacement</u>. Draw a tree diagram and hence find the probability that both disks are the same colour."

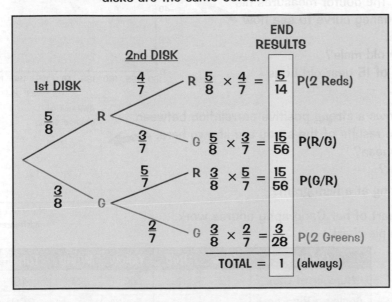

Once the tree diagram is drawn all you then need to do to answer the question is simply select the relevant **END RESULTS** and then **ADD THEM TOGETHER**:

| 2 REDS | (5/14) |
| 2 GREENS | (3/28) |

$$\frac{5}{14} + \frac{3}{28} = \frac{13}{28}$$

If you can, use a calculator for this.

General Tree Diagram reporting for duty sir...

How convenient — answers growing on trees. You still need to learn the <u>general tree diagram</u> and the <u>4 points</u>
that go with it though — just in case there's a disappointing harvest. I'll leave you to have a go at these...

1) OK, let's see what you've learnt shall we: turn over and write down everything you know about tree diagrams.
2) A bag contains 6 red tarantulas and 4 black tarantulas. If two girls each pluck out a tarantula at random,
   draw a tree diagram to find the probability that they get different coloured ones.

Revision Summary

Well, all's well that ends well. So they say. But it's not quite over yet. There's just this one page of harmless questions. I reckon there are some tricky types of graph to get your head round in this Section, so give them some special attention. Oh, and make sure you know what the totals all mean on the frequency tables. Then give these questions a whirl...

Week / Size of shoe	1	2	3	4
5	29	11	17	12
6	21	35	7	16
7	2	17	10	2
8	15	6	2	2

1) Steven works in a shoe shop. His boss wants to know which is the <u>most common</u> size of shoe they've sold this month, and how many of that size they've sold on average per week.
   a) Which two values does Steven need to work out:
   Mean, Median, Mode or Range?
   b) Work out these two values using the information in the table.

2) Name the four main <u>sampling methods</u>, with a brief description of each.

3) Write down seven important details about <u>frequency tables</u>.

4) Jessica's science class are collecting their results in a grouped frequency table. Jessica's result is 5 g. Into which group in the table should her data go?

Mass (g)	$1 < m \leq 5$	$5 < m \leq 10$	$10 < m \leq 15$
Frequency	6	23	5

5) Calum is writing an article on the Skelly Crag half-marathon for the local paper. He wants to include the <u>mean time taken</u>. Estimate the mean time from the table below.

Time (min)	$60 < t \leq 90$	$90 < t \leq 120$	$120 < t \leq 150$	$150 < t \leq 180$	$180 < t \leq 210$	$210 < t \leq 240$
Frequency	15	60	351	285	206	83

6) Why is it <u>not possible</u> to find the exact value of the mean from a grouped frequency table?

7) What is a histogram?

8) What are the three steps of the method for tackling all histograms?

9) Write down the formula for <u>frequency density</u>.

10) Write down four key points about cumulative frequency.

11) Sean goes for a checkup at the doctors. The doctor measures his height and checks it on a cumulative frequency curve to see how he compares with other 15 year old males.
   a) What's the <u>median</u> height for a 15 year old male?
   b) Sean is 180 cm tall. What <u>percentage</u> of 15 year old boys are taller than Sean?

12) A newspaper has claimed that a study shows a strong positive correlation between eating cheese and having nightmares. The results of the study are shown here.
   a) What does <u>strong positive correlation</u> mean?
   b) Do you agree with the newspaper claim?

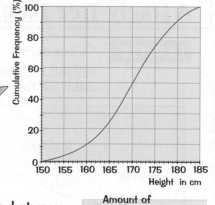

Amount of cheese eaten

Number of nightmares

13) How do you <u>estimate</u> the mean from looking at a histogram?

14) Fiona has carried out a traffic survey as part of her Geography course work. She wants to present the information in a pie chart.
   a) <u>Complete Fiona's table</u>.
   b) Draw the **PIE CHART**.

Colour	Blue	Red	Yellow	White	Totals:
Number of Cars	12	15	4	9	40
Angle on Pie Chart					360°

15) The probability of a biased dice <u>giving a SIX</u> is <u>0.2</u>. What is the chance of it <u>NOT</u> giving a six?

16) What's the formula for relative frequency? What are the AND and OR rules of probability?

17) Jackie is preparing a game for the school fair. She wants the players to have a <u>less than 10% chance</u> of winning to make sure the school doesn't lose much money. In Jackie's game you roll two dice. If you roll two sixes you win £20. Is the chance of winning less than 10%?

18) Write down four important facts about <u>tree diagrams</u>. Draw a general one with all the features on it.

Answers

Section One

P.2 Prime Numbers:
2) a) 101, 103, 107, 109   **b)** none   **c)** 503, 509

P.3 Common Factors:
1) 1, 2, 3, 4, 6, 12   **2)** 1, 2, 4, 8   HCF = 8

P.4 Common Multiples:
1) 7, 14, 21, 28, 35, 42, 49, 56, 63, 70
2) e.g. 12, 24, 36, 48   **3)** 60

P.5 Square Roots and Cube Roots:
1) a) 14.14 **b)** 20, other value in a) is -14.14
2) a) g = 6 or -6 **b)** b = 4 **c)** r = 3 or -3

P.6 Order of Operations:
1) a) 12 **b)** 39.96

P.7 Using Calculators:
1) a) 11/4 **b)** 33/2 **c)** 33/4

P.9 Standard Form:
1) a) 8.54×10^5 **b)** 0.00456
2) a) 2×10^{11} **b)** 1×10^8 **3)** 6.5×10^{102}

P.10 Sets:
1) Elements in set B are 1, 4, 9, 16, 25, 36, 49, 64, 81, 100.   22 ∉ B.

P.11 Sets:
1) a) P = {2, 4, 6, 8, 10, 12} **b)** n(Q) = 4
c) P ∪ Q = {2, 3, 4, 6, 8, 9, 10, 12} **d)** P ∩ Q = {6, 12}
e) n(P ∩ Q) = 2

P.12 Sets:
1) a) S′ = {2, 3, 5, 6, 7, 8, 10, 11, 12, 13, 14, 15, 17, 18, 19} **b)** e.g. if A = {1, 4}, A ⊂ S

Revision Summary for Section One

6) no, 161 ÷ 7 = 23   **7)** 1, 2, 3, 6, 7, 14, 21, 42
8) 1, 2, 3, 6 **9)** 7 **10)** 13, 26, 39, 52, 65, 78, 91, 104, 117, 130 **11)** e.g. 36, 72, 108 **12)** 84
13) a) +16, −16 **b)** 6 **c)** +18, −18 **14)** +6, −6
16) 17 **17)** 5(6 + 11) **18)** 23/4
19) a) 9.7×10^5 **b)** 6.83×10^6 **c)** 3.56×10^9
20) 0.00000275 **21)** 3, 4, 5, 6, 7, 8, 9, 10, 11
22) a) n(W) = 50 **b)** H = ∅ **c)** Cheddar ∈ Z **d)** F ⊈ G
23)

A ∪ B = {1, 3, 5, 6, 7, 8, 9},
A ∩ B = {5, 7, 9},
n(A ∪ B) = 7, C = {1, 3}

Venn diagram: A {1. 3.}, intersection {5. 7. 9.}, B {6. 8.}

24) a) everyone at her school, 222 elements **b)** 28 **c)** 126
d) 141, the number of people who don't like limeade
e) 111

Section Two

P.14 Fractions, Decimals and Percentages:
1) a) 6/10 = 3/5 **b)** 2/100 = 1/50 **c)** 77/100
d) 555/1000 = 111/200 **e)** 56/10 = 28/5 or 5 3/5

P.15 Fractions, Decimals and Percentages:
1) 1/7   **2) a)** terminating **b)** recurring **c)** terminating

P.16 Fractions:
1) a) 5/32 **b)** 32/35 **c)** 23/20 or 1 3/20 **d)** 1/40
e) 167/27 or 6 5/27   **2) a)** 220 **b)** £1.75

P.17 Multiplying and Dividing Decimals:
1) 179.2 **2)** 6.12 **3)** 56.1 **4)** 56 **5)** 46 **6)** 12

P.18 Speed, Distance and Time:
1) 1 hr 37 mins 30 secs **2)** 1.89 km = 1890 m

P.20 Ratios:
1) a) 5:7 **b)** 2:3 **c)** 3:5   **2)** 17½ bowls of porridge
3) £3500 : £2100 : £2800

P.21 Proportion:
1) £4.40 **2)** 14 minutes

P.22 Percentages:
1) 40% **2)** £20 500

P.23 Time:
1) 5:15 p.m. **2)** 4:05 p.m. **3)** 1,440 ; 86,400
4) 3hrs 30 min; 5hrs 45 min

P.24 Measures:
1) 7 hrs 11 min **2)** 2300 m **3)** 20 m

P.26 Money Questions:
1) Large size is best value at 1.90 g per penny.   **2)** £34

P.27 Interest:
1) a) £112 **b)** £112.55   **2)** £2000

P.28 Household Finance:
1) 21%

P.29 Rounding Numbers:
1) 3.57 **2)** 0.05 **3)** 12.910 **4)** 3546.1

P.30 Rounding Numbers:
1) a) 3.41 **b)** 1.05 **c)** 0.07 **d)** 3.60
2 a) 568 **b)** 23400 **c)** 0.0456 **d)** 0.909
3) a) 35 g **b)** 134 km/h **c)** 850 g

P.31 Estimating:
1) Approx 7 cm × 7 cm × 10 cm = 490 cm³
2) a) 3.4 or 3.5 **b)** 10.1 or 10.2 **c)** 7.1, 7.2 or 7.3
d) 5.4 or 5.5

P.32 Accuracy and Measuring:
1) 16.95 m up to 17.05 m
2 a) x — lower bound 2.315 m, upper bound 2.325 m
y — lower bound 0.445 m, upper bound 0.455 m
b) max value of z = 4.57, min value of z = 4.51

Revision Summary for Section Two

1) 645/1000 = 129/200   **3) a)** 320 **b)** £60 **c)** 195
4) a) 88/30 = 44/15 = 2 14/15 **b)** 75/48 = 25/16 = 1 9/16
c) 23/8 = 2 7/8 **d)** 11/21
5) a) 9.68 **b)** 13.57 **c)** 4.1 **d)** 15 **9)** 240
11) Jill £18, Heather £15 and Susie £9 **14)** £3710
15) £58.75 **16)** No, it would cost £36 **17)** 5.20 p.m.
18) 10.6 hours **21)** Biggest is best buy at 4.8 g per penny
22) £20.63 **23)** £140.26 **24)** £17.33
25) 3.7, 8.4, 5.7, 5.9
27) a) 56.5 m, 55.5 m, 22.5 m, 21.5 m
b) minimum = 1193.25 m², maximum = 1271.25 m²

Answers

Section Three

P.34 Conversion Graphs and Gradients:
1) 23-24 km   **2)** 25 miles

P.35 D/T and S/T Graphs:
1) 0.5 km/h **2)** Accelerations: 6 m/s^2, 2 m/s^2, -8 m/s^2 (deceleration); Speeds: 30 m/s, 50 m/s

P.36 Coordinates, Lines and Line Segments:
1) A(4,5) B(6,0) C(5,-5) D(0,-3)
E(-5,-2) F(-4,0) G(-3,3) H(0,5)

P.37 Midpoints and Lengths of Line Segments:
1) a) (5, 2.5)   **b)** (-2, 2.5)   **c)** (0, -3.5)   **2)** 5 units

P.39 Plotting Straight Line Graphs:
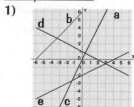

P.40 Finding the Gradient:
1) -1.5

P.41 y = mx + c:
1)
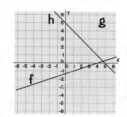

P.42 Quadratic Graphs:
1)
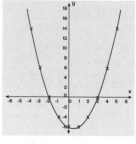
Using graph, solutions are x = -2 and x = 3.

P.43 Some Harder Graphs to Learn:
1) a) x^2 bucket shape
b) –x^3 wiggle (top left to bottom right)
c) +ve inverse proportion graph
d) circle about origin, radius 6
e) –ve inverse proportion graph
f) +x^3 wiggle (bottom left to top right)
g) –x^2 upside down bucket shape
h) K^x curve upwards through (0,1)

Revision Summary for Section Three

1) a) 1 litre   **b)** 2.8 pints   **3)** 2 cm^3 / min

10)
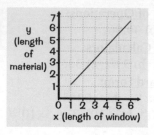

12) a) A straight line
b)

x	1	3	6
y	1.1	3.3	6.6

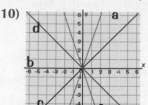

Section Four

P.45 Powers and Roots:
1) a) 3^8 **b)** 4 **c)** 8^{12} **d)** 1 **e)** 7^6
2) a) 64 **b)** 1/625 **c)** 1/5 **d)** 2 **e)** 125 **f)** 1/25
3) a) 1.53×10^{17} **b)** 15.9 **c)** 2.89

P.46 Finding the nth Term:
1) a) 3n + 1 **b)** 5n – 2 **c)** ½n(n + 1) **d)** n^2 – 2n + 4

P.47 Basic Algebra:
1) a) +12 **b)** -6 **c)** x **d)** -3
2) a) +18 **b)** -216 **c)** 2 **d)** -27 **e)** -336
3) a) (x – 4y)(x + 4y) **b)** (7 – 9pq)(7 + 9pq)
c) 3(2yx^3 – 4k^{2}m^4)(2yx^3 + 4k^{2}m^4)
= 12(yx^3 – 2k^{2}m^4)(yx^3 + 2k^{2}m^4)

P.49 Basic Algebra:
1) 4x + y – 4   **2)** 6p^{2}q – 8pq^3 **3)** 8g^2 + 16g – 10
4) 7xy^2(2xy + 3 – 5x^{2}y^2)   **5)** c^4/6d^3 **6)** $\dfrac{2(17g - 6)}{5(3g - 4)}$

P.50 Making Formulas from Words:
1) y = 5x – 3   **2)** A = $\dfrac{6h + t}{2}$ – 5

P.51 Solving Equations:
1) a) x = 2   **b)** x = - 0.2 or -1/5   **c)** x = ±3

P.52 Rearranging Formulas:
1) C = 5(F – 32)/9   **2) a)** p = -4y/3 **b)** p = rq/(r + q)
c) p = ± $\sqrt{\dfrac{rq}{(r + q)}}$

P.53 Simultaneous Equations:
1) F = 3, G = -1

P.54 Direct and Inverse Proportion:
1) a) E.g. Total cost vs No. of tins of Bone-tingling Fireball Soup **b)** E.g. no. of people working on a job vs time taken to complete it.

Answers

P.55 Variation:
1) 0.632 Hz, 40.8 cm
P.57 Factorising Quadratics:
1) a) x = 3 or -8   **b)** x = 7 or -1   **c)** x = 1 or -7
d) x = 4 or -3/5
P.58 The Quadratic Formula:
1) a) x = 0.39 or -10.39   **b)** x = 1.46 or -0.46
c) x = 0.44 or -3.44
P.59 Completing the Square:
1) a) x = 0.39 or -10.39   **b)** x = 1.46 or -0.46
c) x = 0.44 or -3.44
P.60 Functions:
1) a) 19 **b)** 7 **c)** 10 – 10x **d)** $5x^2 + 14$
e) –16 **f)** 84 **g)** (x + 1) / 5 **h)** (9 – 5x) / 2
P.61 Inequalities:
1) $-2 \leq x$ **2) a)** -6, -5, -4, -3, -2, -1, 0, 1, 2, 3, 4, 5, 6
b) -4, -3, -2, -1, 0, 1, 2, 3, 4
P.63 Linear Programming:
2) Optimum point is as shown — i.e. K=150 and S=150 giving an income of £750

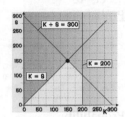

Revision Summary for Section Four
1) 3, –3   **3) a)** 6n – 7 **b)** 53   **11)** y = 2x + 4
13) a) 4.20 = 6x + 3y, 5.32 = 10x + 2y **b)** £6.72

Section Five

P.65 Symmetry:
1) H: 2 lines of symmetry, Rot[nl]. symmetry Order 2,
N: 0 lines of symmetry, Rot[nl]. symmetry Order 2
E: 1 line of symmetry, no Rotational symmetry,
Y: 1 line of symmetry, no Rot[nl]. symmetry
M: 1 line of symmetry, no Rotational symmetry,
S: 0 lines of symmetry, Rot[nl]. symmetry Order 2,
T: 1 line of symmetry, no Rot[nl]. symmetry
2) Left to right, no of planes of symmetry are:
∞, 9 (this one is the hardest, by the way), 3, 4, ∞, 4
P.67 Regular Polygons:
3) 72°, 108° **4)** 30°, 150°
P.68 Areas:
1) Perimeter 27.5 cm, area 35 cm²
P.69 Surface Area and Volume:
1) a) Triangular Prism, V = 27 m³, Surface Area = 78 m²
b) Trapezoidal Prism, V = 148.5 cm³,
Surface Area = 196.8 cm²
P.70 Surface Area and Volume:
1) a) Cylinder, V = 0.70 m³ **b)** Cone, 20.3 m³
2) Ping pong ball: V = 33.5 cm³, Surface area = 50.3 cm²
tennis ball: V = 179.6 cm³, Surface area = 153.9 cm²
P.72 Similarity and Enlargements:
1) A'(-3,-1.5),   B'(-7.5,-3), C'(-6,-6)   **2)** 64 m²

Revision Summary for Section Five
5) 45°, 135°   **7)** £1008   **14)** 213.628 cm²   **15)** 125
20) 3   **21)** 150 cm wide, 300 cm long, 250 cm high.

Section Six

P.78 Vectors:
1) a) –**m** – **b**   **b)** ½**b** – ½**a** + **m** (=½AC)
c) ½(**a** – **b**) + **m**   **d)** ½(**b** – **a**)
P.79 Vectors:
1) a) 5.39   **b)** 4.24   **c)** 8.06   **2)** 26.6°
P.80 Matrices:
1) a) $\begin{pmatrix} 3 & 8 \\ 4 & -7 \end{pmatrix}$ **b)** $\begin{pmatrix} -5 & -2 \\ 8 & -11 \end{pmatrix}$ **c)** $\begin{pmatrix} 12 & 15 \\ -6 & 6 \end{pmatrix}$

d) $\begin{pmatrix} 1 & -3 \\ -6 & 9 \end{pmatrix}$ **e)** $\begin{pmatrix} 26 & -33 \\ 14 & -24 \end{pmatrix}$ **f)** $\begin{pmatrix} -10 & 1 \\ 42 & 12 \end{pmatrix}$
P.81 Matrices:
1) a) $-\frac{1}{8}\begin{pmatrix} 5 & -2 \\ -9 & 2 \end{pmatrix}$ **b)** $\begin{pmatrix} 9 & -7 \\ 4 & -3 \end{pmatrix}$ **c)** $\frac{1}{23}\begin{pmatrix} 3 & 1 \\ -8 & 5 \end{pmatrix}$
P.83 The Six Transformations:
1) A→B Rotation of 90° clockwise about the origin,
B→C Reflection in the line y = x,
C→A Reflection in the y-axis,   **A→D** Translation of $\begin{pmatrix} -9 \\ -7 \end{pmatrix}$
2) A'→B, Rotation of 180° clockwise or anticlockwise
about the point (0,3).
P.84 Matrix Transformations:
1) A→C: $\begin{pmatrix} -1 & 0 \\ 0 & 1 \end{pmatrix}$,   **B→A:** $\begin{pmatrix} 0 & -1 \\ 1 & 0 \end{pmatrix}$
P.86 Geometry:
1) 68° and 44°, or both 56°   **2)** x = 66°

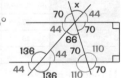

P.88 Circle Geometry:
1) BCD = 90°, CBO = 42°, OBE = 48°, BOE = 84°,
OEF = 90°, AEB = 42°, DOE = 96°, BEO = 48°, CBE = 90°,
BEF = 138°, AEO = 90°
P.89 Pythagoras' Theorem and Bearings:
1) BC = 8 m   **2)** 298°   **3)** 118°
P.91 Trigonometry — Sin, Cos, Tan:
1) x = 26.5 m   **2)** 23.6°   **3)** 32.6° (both)
P.92 3D Pythagoras and Trigonometry:
1) 25.1° **2)** 7.07 cm
P.94 The Sine and Cosine Rules:
2) 17.13 m, 68.8°, 41.2°
P.95 Sine and Cosine for Larger Angles:
1) a) 150° **b)** 172.8° (to 1 d.p.)   **c)** 101.5° (to 1 d.p.)
2) B = 64.1° or 115.9°

Answers

Revision Summary for Section Six

9) a) $\begin{pmatrix} 30 & 46 \\ 12 & 19 \end{pmatrix}$ **b)** Inverse of $\underline{C} = \begin{pmatrix} -2 & 5 \\ 1 & -2 \end{pmatrix}$,

inverse of $\underline{D} = \dfrac{-1}{18}\begin{pmatrix} 8 & -3 \\ -6 & 0 \end{pmatrix}$

11) C→D, Reflection in the y-axis, and an enlargement SF 2, centre the origin **12) D→C**, Reflection in the y-axis, and an enlargement SF ½, centre the origin.
18) 4.72 m **21)** 41°

Section Seven

P.97 Mean, Median, Mode and Range:
First: -14, -12, -5, -5, 0, 1, 3, 6, 7, 8, 10, 14, 18, 23, 25
Mean = 5.27, Median = 6, Mode = -5, Range = 39

P.98 Sampling Methods:
1) Sample too small, motorways not representative of average motorist, only done at one time of day in one place.
Better approach: Take samples from a range of different locations across the country, take samples at different times of day, have a much larger sample size, e.g. 1000.

P.100 Frequency Tables:

No. of phones	0	1	2	3	4	5	6	TOTALS
Frequency	1	25	53	34	22	5	1	141
No. × Frequency	0	25	106	102	88	25	6	352

Mean = 2.5, Median = 2, Mode = 2, Range = 6

P.101 Grouped Frequency Tables:

Length L (cm)	15.5≤L<16.5	16.5≤L<17.5	17.5≤L<18.5	18.5≤L<19.5	TOTALS
Frequency	12	18	23	8	61
Mid-Interval Value	16	17	18	19	-
Freq × MIV	192	306	414	152	1064

1) Mean = 17.4
2) Modal Group = 17.5 ≤ L < 18.5, Median ≈ 17.5

P.102 Histograms and Frequency Density:
1) 32 sunflowers

P.103 Cumulative Frequency:

No. of fish	41 – 45	46 – 50	51 – 55	56 – 60	61 – 65	66 – 70	71 – 75
Frequency	2	7	17	25	19	8	2
Cum. Freq.	2	9	26	51	70	78	80

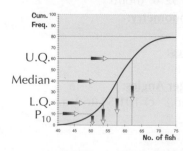

Median = 58, Lower Quartile = 53, Upper Quartile = 62, Interquartile Range = 9, Tenth Percentile = 51

P.104 Spread of Data:
1)
2)

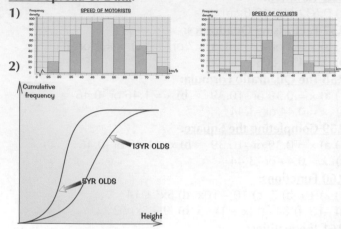

P.106 Other Graphs and Charts:
2) Guinea Pigs 68°, Rabbits 60°, Ducks 104°, Stick insects 48°

P.107 Probability:

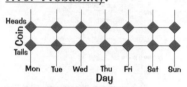

P.108 Probability:
1) 1/5 or 20% or 0.2

P.109 Relative Frequency:
1) Landing on red: 0.43, landing on blue: 0.24, landing on green: 0.33

P.110 Probability — Multiple Events:
1) a) Probability = QQA+QAQ+AQQ = (4/52)(3/51)(1/50) + (4/52)(1/51)(3/50) + (1/52)(4/51)(3/50) = 3/11050
b) Probability
= (4/52) × (3/51) + (4/52) × (3/51) + (4/52) × (3/51)
= 3 × (4/52) × (3/51) = 3/221

P.111 Probability — Tree Diagrams:
2) 8/15

Revision Summary for Section Seven
1) a) Mode and mean **b)** Mode = size 6, Mean = 20 pairs
4) 1 < m ≤ 5 **5)** 161 min **11) a)** 170 cm **b)** 10%
12) a) Both things increase or decrease together and they're closely related. **b)** No
14) a) Angles are: Blue 108°, Red 135°, Yellow 36°, White 81°. **b)**

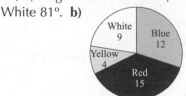

15) 0.8 **17)** Yes

Index

Index